HIDDEN GOLD

THE CENTRAL NORSEMAN STORY

MONOGRAPH SERIES

1.	* Detrital Heavy Minerals in Natural Accumulates	*George Baker*	*1962*
2.	Research in Chemical and Extraction Metallurgy	*Ed. J. T. Woodcock, A.E. Jenkins and G. M. Willis*	*1967*
3.	* Broken Hill Mines – 1968	*Ed. M. Radmanovich and J. T. Woodcock*	*1968*
4.	* Economic Geology of New Zealand	*Ed. G. J. Williams*	*1974*
5.	Economic Geology of Australia and Papua New Guinea – 1. Metals	*Ed. C. L. Knight*	*1975*
6.	* Economic Geology of Australia and Papua New Guinea – 2. Coal	*Ed. D. M. Traves and D. King*	*1975*
7.	* Economic Geology of Australia and Papua New Guinea – 3. Petroleum	*Ed. R. B. Leslie, H. J. Evans and C. L. Knight*	*1976*
8.	* Economic Geology of Australia and Papua New Guinea – 4. Industrial Minerals and Rocks	*Ed. C. L. Knight*	*1976*
9.	Field Geologists' Manual (Third Edition)	*Ed. D. A. Berkman*	*1989*
10.	* Mining and Metallurgical Practices in Australasia (The Sir Maurice Mawby Memorial Volume)	*Ed. J.T. Woodcock*	*1980*
11.	Victoria's Brown Coal – A Huge Fortune in Chancery (The Sir Willis Connolly Memorial Volume)	*Ed. J.T. Woodcock*	*1984*
12.	Australasian Coal Mining Practice	*Ed. C.H. Martin*	*1986*
13.	Mineral Deposits of New Zealand	*Ed. D. Kear*	*1989*
14.	Geology of the Mineral Deposits of Australia and Papua New Guinea	*Ed. F. Hughes*	*1990*
15.	The Rocks Speak	*H. F. King*	*1989*
16.	Hidden Gold – The Central Norseman Story	*J. D. Campbell*	*1990*

Key: * = Out of Print

Copies of all books currently in print can be obtained from
The Australasian Institute of Mining and Metallurgy
Clunies Ross House 191 Royal Parade Parkville Victoria Australia 3052
Telephone (03) 347 3166; Facsimile (03) 347 8525.

Volume 2
ISBN 0 949106 46 1

First published in 1990

Cover photographs – A Central Norseman gold quartz sample.

Designed and printed in Australia by James Squire Color Printing
76 Chestnut Street Richmond Victoria Australia 3121

HIDDEN GOLD

THE CENTRAL NORSEMAN STORY

An account of Structural Geological Studies and Ore-search
at Norseman, Western Australia

J. D. CAMPBELL

VOLUME TWO
Figures and Plates
to accompany volume one

INCORPORATED BY ROYAL CHARTER 1955

MONOGRAPH 16

Published by
THE AUSTRALASIAN INSTITUTE OF MINING AND METALLURGY
CLUNIES ROSS HOUSE 191 ROYAL PARADE PARKVILLE VICTORIA AUSTRALIA 3052

The generous support of Western Mining Corporation Holdings Limited and
Central Norseman Gold Corporation Limited is gratefully acknowledged

CONTENTS

SECOND OF TWO VOLUMES

SCALES OF FIGURES

1.	1 in. = 1 mile
2.	1 in. = 2,000 ft.
3.	–
4.	1 in. = 400 ft.
5A.	1 in. = 500 ft.
5B.	1 in. = 400 ft.
6A-B.	1 in. = 200 ft.
6C-D.	1 in. = 800 ft.
7.	1 in. = 400 ft.
8.	1 in. = 1,000 ft.
9A.	1 in. = 1,000 ft.
9B-C.	–
10.	1 in. = 1,250 ft.
11.	1 in. = 800 ft.
12.	1 in. = 2,000 ft.
13.	–
14.	1 in. = 1,000 ft.
15.	1 in. = 1,000 ft.
16.	1 in. = 800 ft.
17A.	1 in. = 400 ft.
17B-H.	–
18(1-3).	1 in. = 2,000 ft.
18(4).	1 in. = 400 ft.
19.	1 in. = 2,000 ft.
20A.	1 : 10,000
20B.	1 : 5,000
21A.	1 : 5,000
21B.	1 : 10,000
22A.	1 : 10,000
22B.	1 : 5,000
23.	1 in. = 1 mile
24.	1 : 10,000
25A.	1 : 10,000
25B.	1 : 5,000
26A.	1 : 10,000
26B.	1 : 5,000
27.	1 : 5,000
28.	1 : 2,500
29.	1 : 5,000
30.	1 : 5,000
31.	1 : 10,000
32.	1 : 10,000
33.	1 : 10,000
34.	1 : 5,000
35.	1 : 5,000
36.	1 : 10,000
37A-B.	1 : 5,000
38A-B.	1 : 10,000
38C.	1 : 5,000
39.	1 : 10,000
40.	1 : 5,000
41.	1 : 20,000
42.	1 : 20,000
43A.	1 : 20,000
43B-C.	1 : 5,000
44.	1 : 20,000
45A-B.	1 : 10,000
45C.	1 : 20,000
46.	1 : 10,000
47.	1 : 20,000
48A-B.	1 : 10,000
48C.	1 : 20,000
49A.	1 : 10,000
49B.	1 : 20,000
50.	1 : 10,000
51.	1 : 15,000
52.	1 : 15,000
53.	1 : 15,000
54.	1 : 10,000
55.	1 : 20,000
56.	1 : 5,000
57A.	1 : 20,000
57B.	1 : 32,000
58.	1 : 40,000
59.	1 in. = 1 mile
60.	1 : 25,000
61.	–

SCALES OF PLATES

1.	1 in. = 400ft.
2.	1 in. = 800 ft.
3.	1 in. = 1,000 ft.
4.	1 in. = 1,000 ft.
5.	1 in. = 2,000 ft.
6.	1 in. = 2,000 ft.
7A-B.	1 : 5,000
7 keymap	1 : 20,000
8.	1 : 10,000
9.	1 : 5,000
10.	1 : 10,000
11.	1 : 10,000
12.	1 : 10,000
13.	1 : 15,000
14.	1 : 15,000
15A.	1 : 20,000
15B-C.	1 : 15,000
16A.	–
16B-D.	1 : 30,000
17.	1 : 40,000
18A-B.	1 : 40,000
18C.	1 : 80,000
19.	1 : 40,000
20.	–

NOTE: A printing error has occurred in Plate 13A.
The colour in the legend should be red, not pink.

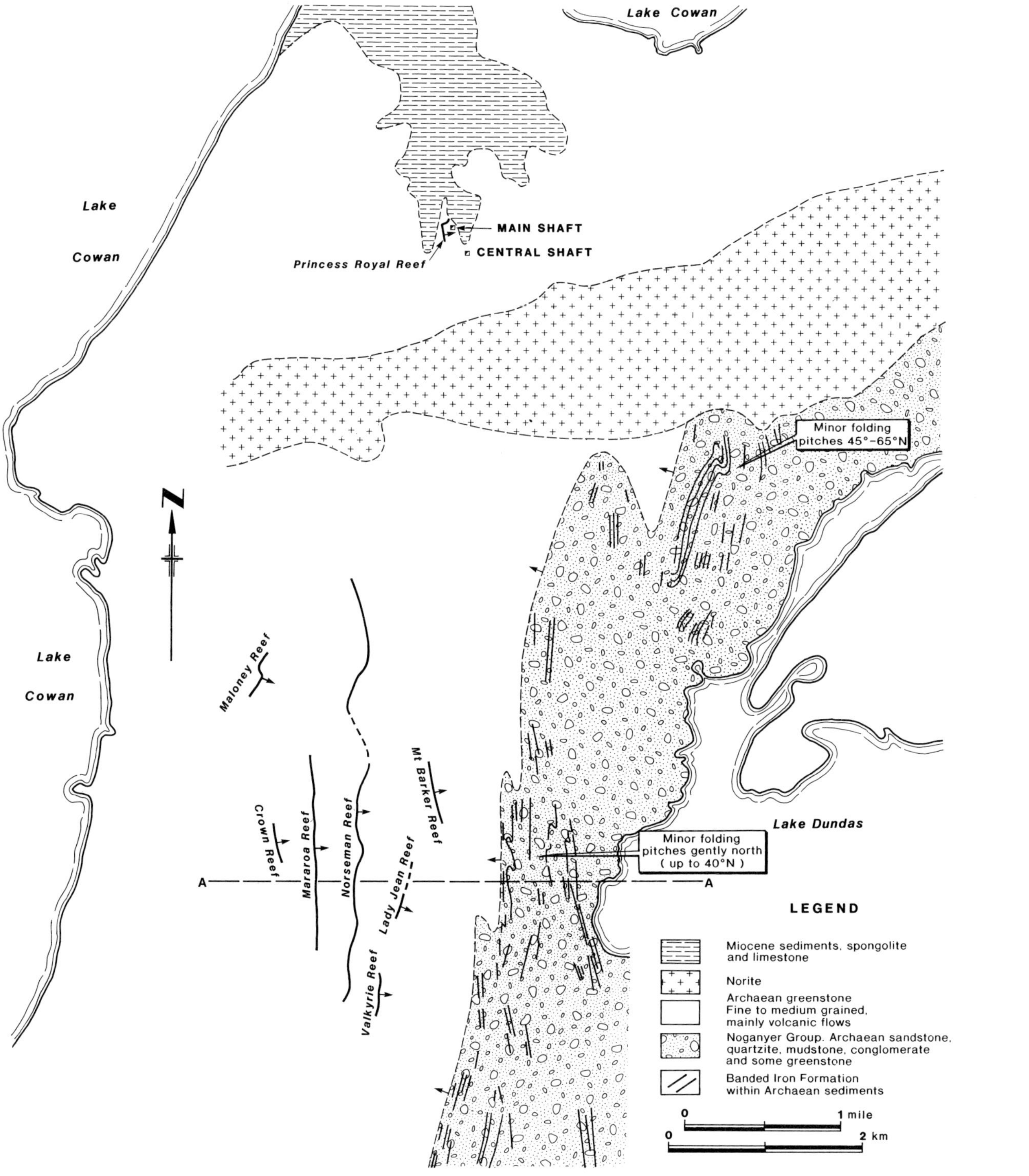

Figure 1 Surface geological map of the main mining area at Norseman, after H.W.B. Talbot.

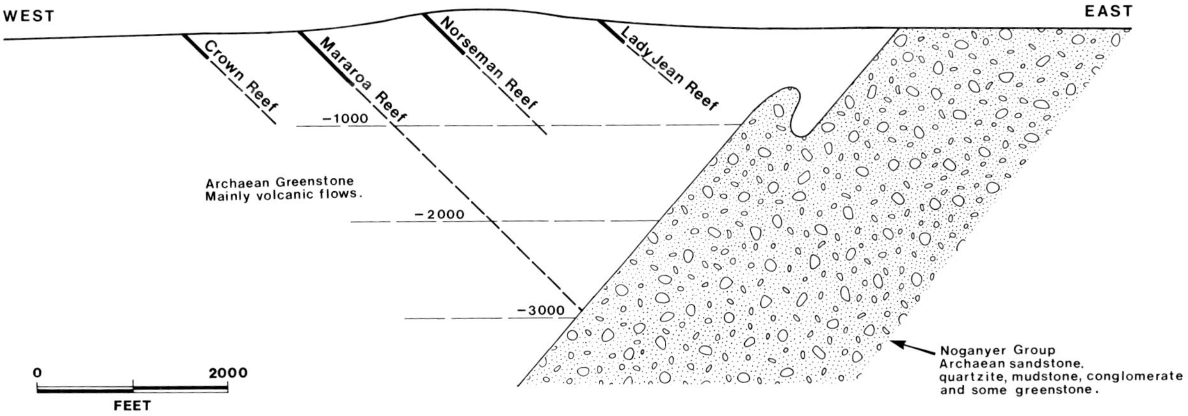

Figure 2

Figure 2 Sketch cross section looking north along line A-A of Figure 1.

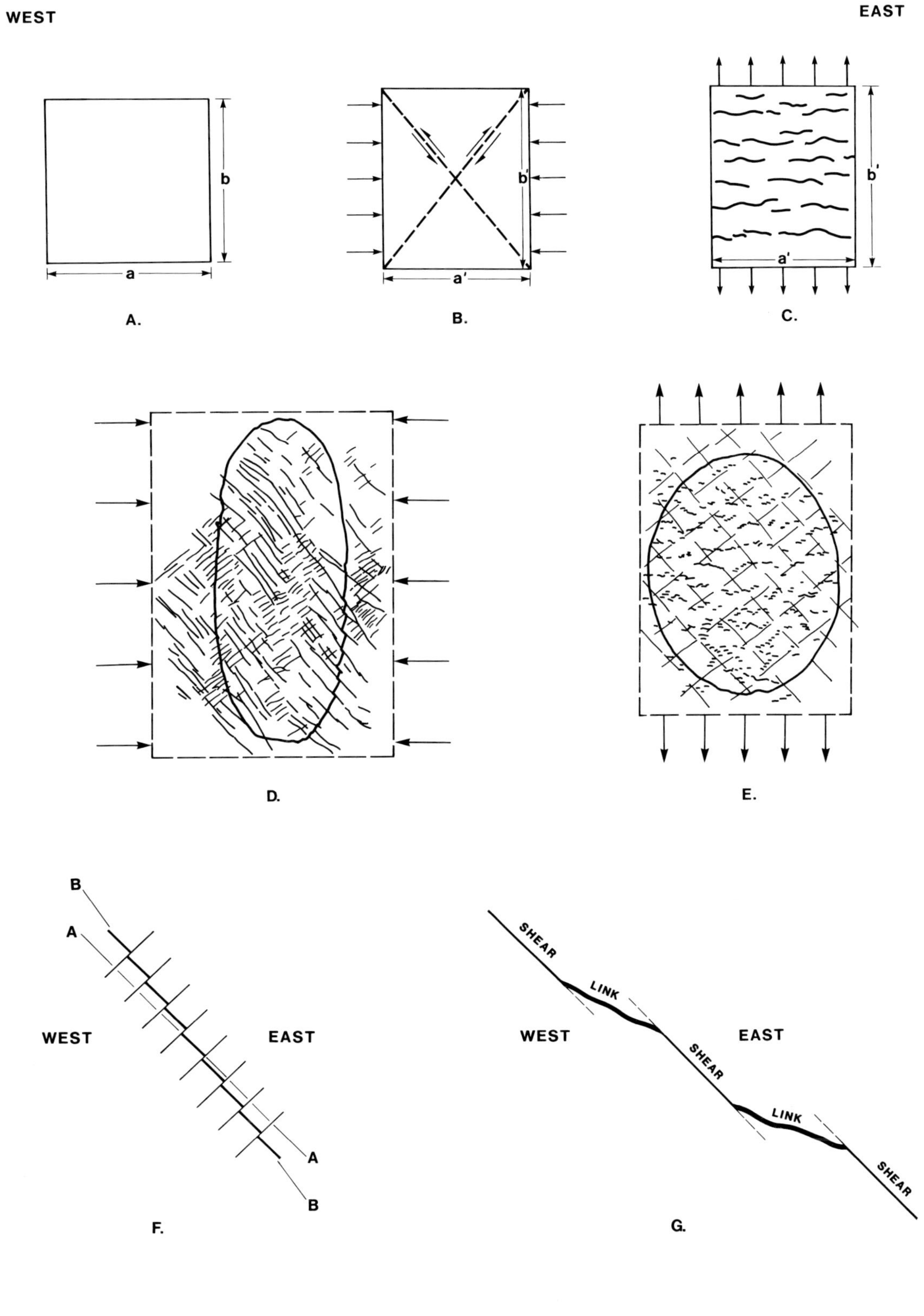

Figure 3 Fracture patterns due to compression and tension.
A, B and C described in text.
D. and E. Experimental demonstrations by H. Cloos;
D. shearing, E. tension fracturing.
F. Rotation of shear A-A to B-B by west-dipping shearing.
G. The normal type of shear-link pattern at Norseman.
(Note: width of links greatly exaggerated).

Figure 3

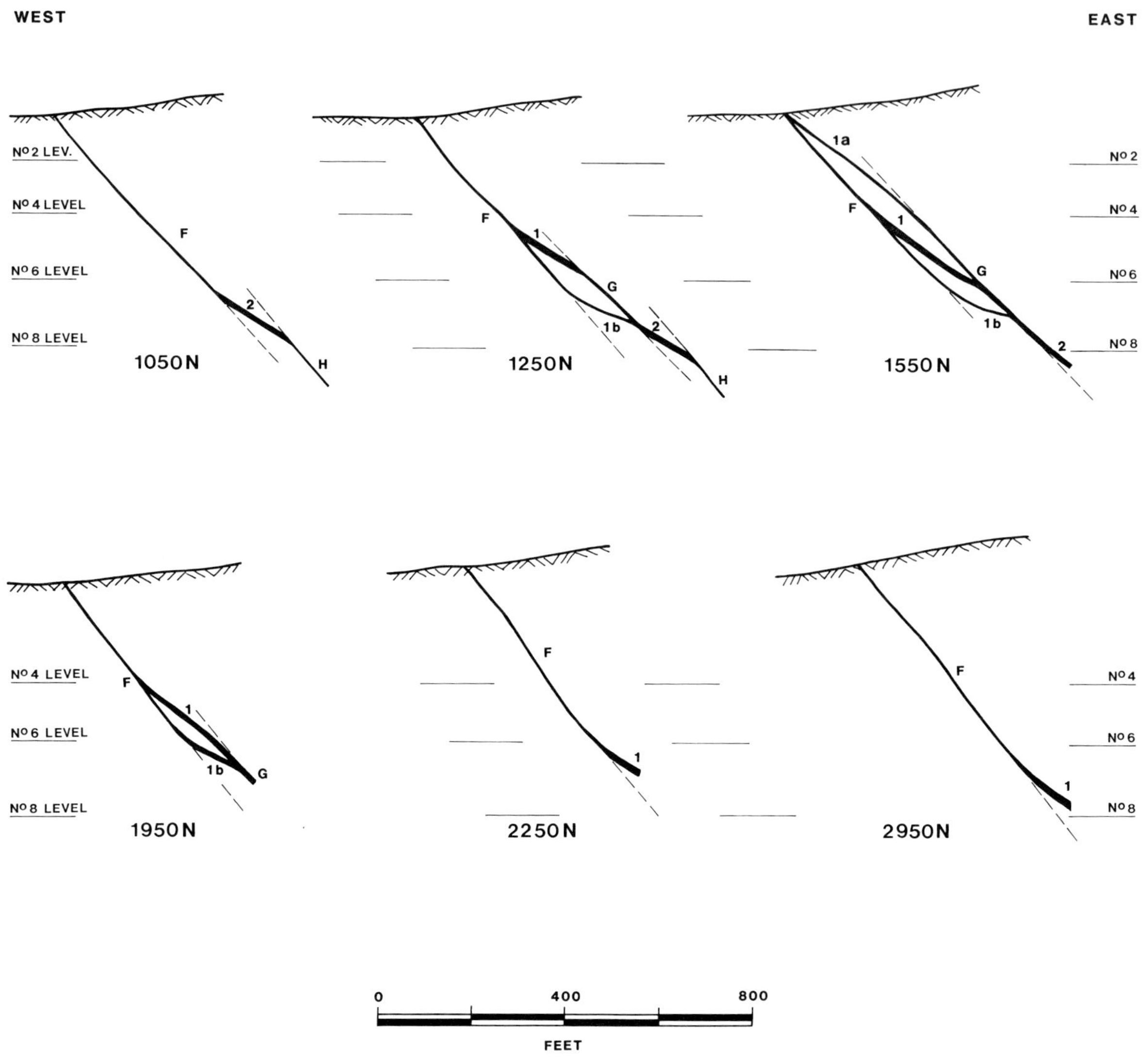

Figure 4

Figure 4 Cross sections of the Mararoa reef looking north. These lie at the positions shown in Plate 1B.

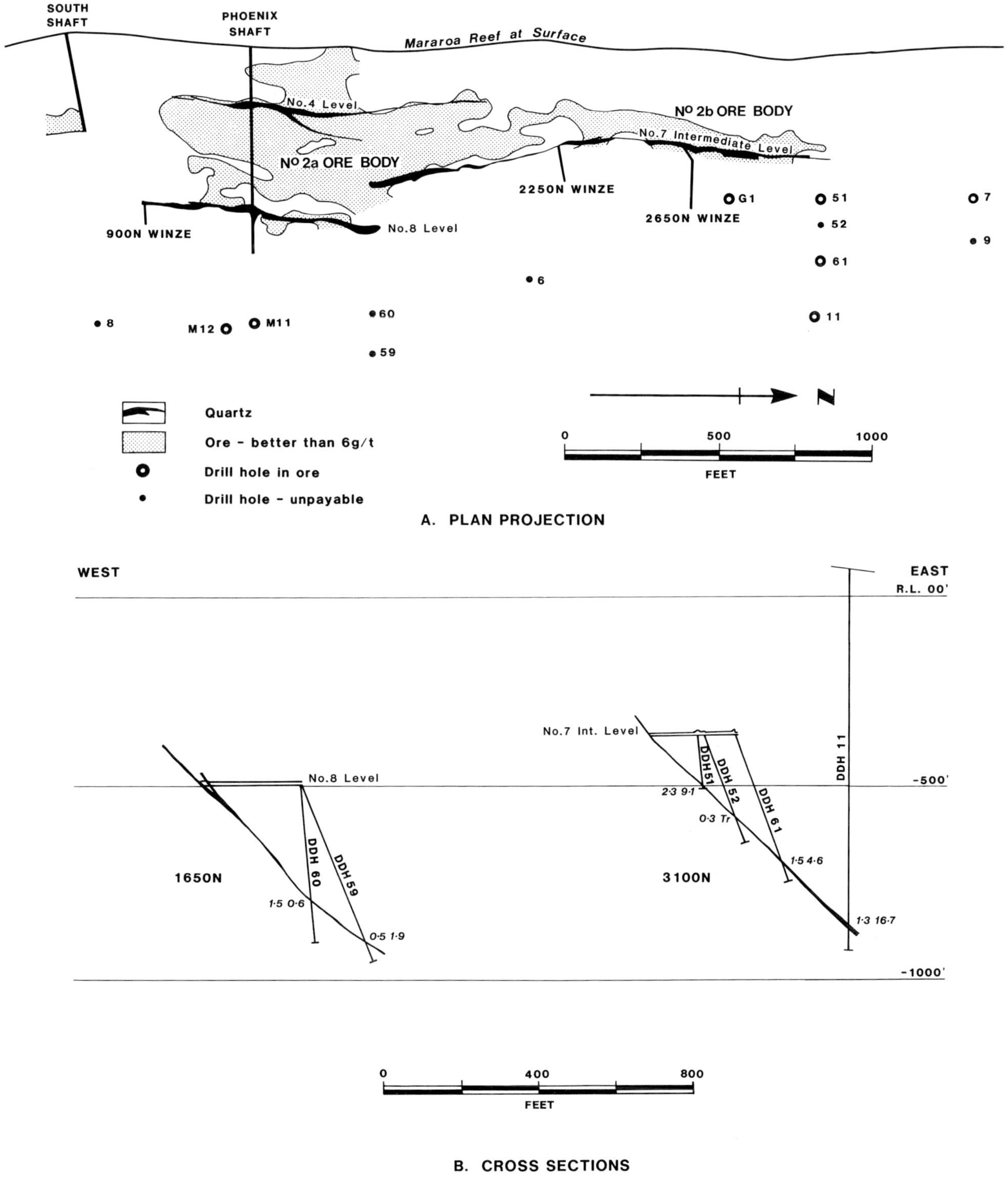

Figure 5 A. Plan projection showing exploration results on the Mararoa reef as at December, 1934 (winze results in text).
B. Cross sections looking north showing the results of diamond drilling.

Figure 5

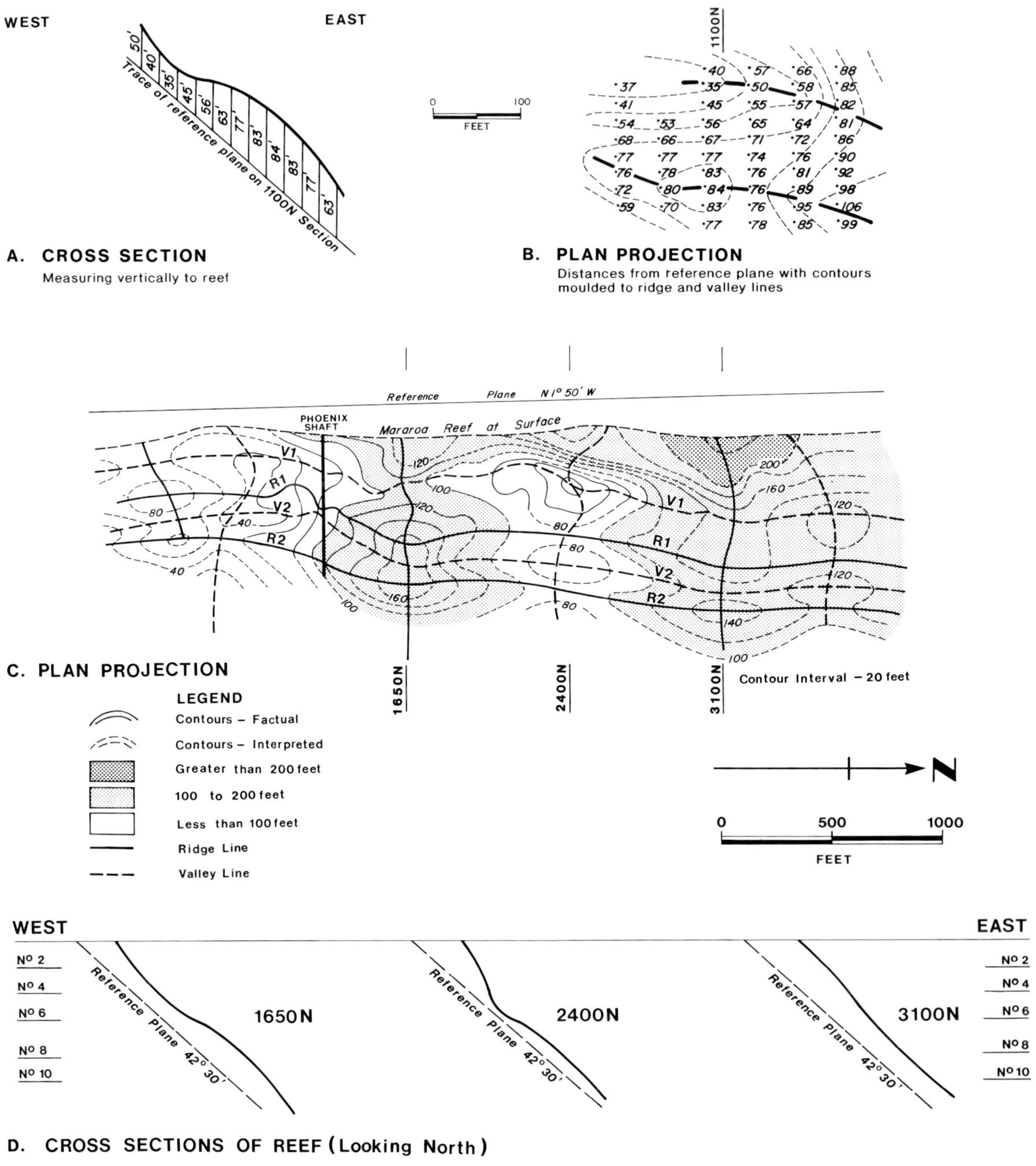

Figure 6

Figure 6 H.J.C. Conolly's vein contouring versus an inclined plane.
A. and B. The basic elements of the method.
C. Plan projection of the Mararoa reef showing the contouring of the mine area and its environs.
D. Cross sections at key positions in Figure 6C.

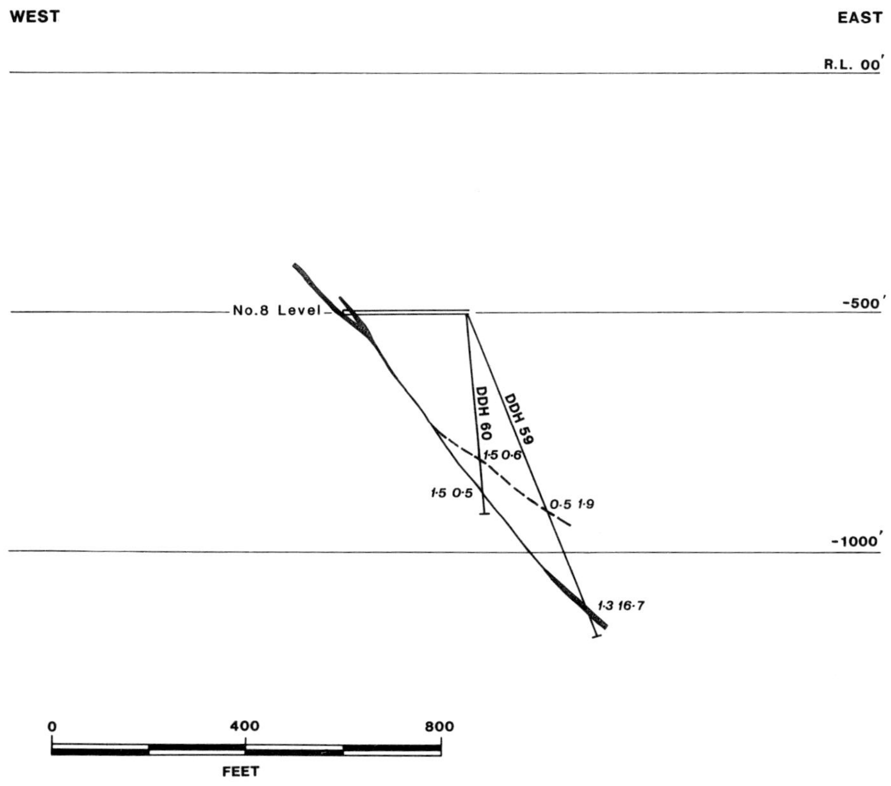

Figure 7 Cross section at 1650N looking north showing the extension of diamond drill hole No. 59 and the changed view of the reef pattern.

Figure 7

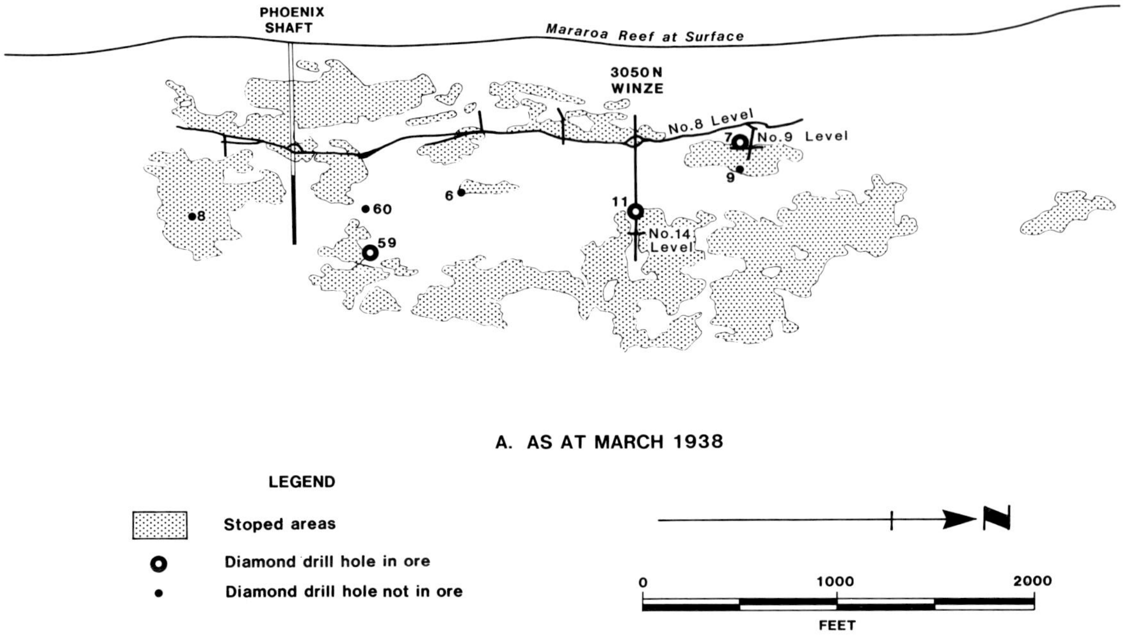

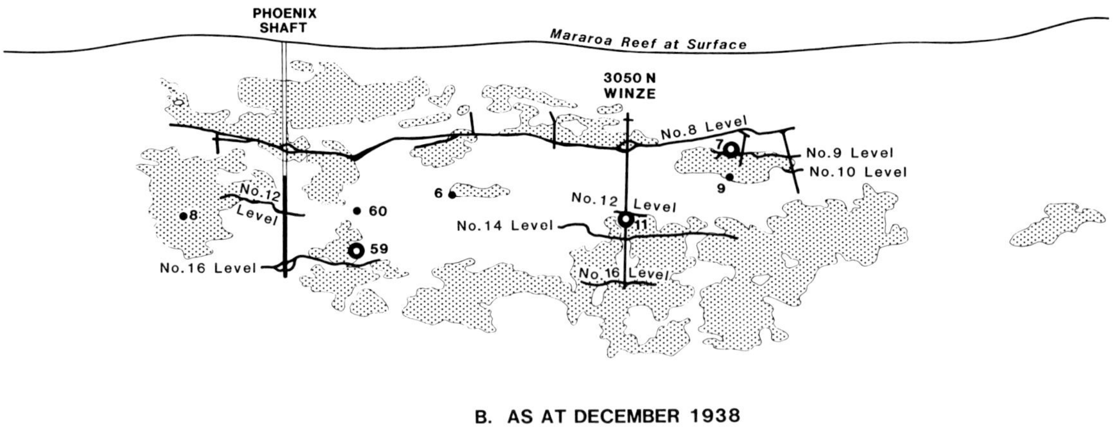

Figure 8

Figure 8 **Plan projections showing mine development on the Mararoa reef in relation to final stoping outlines.**

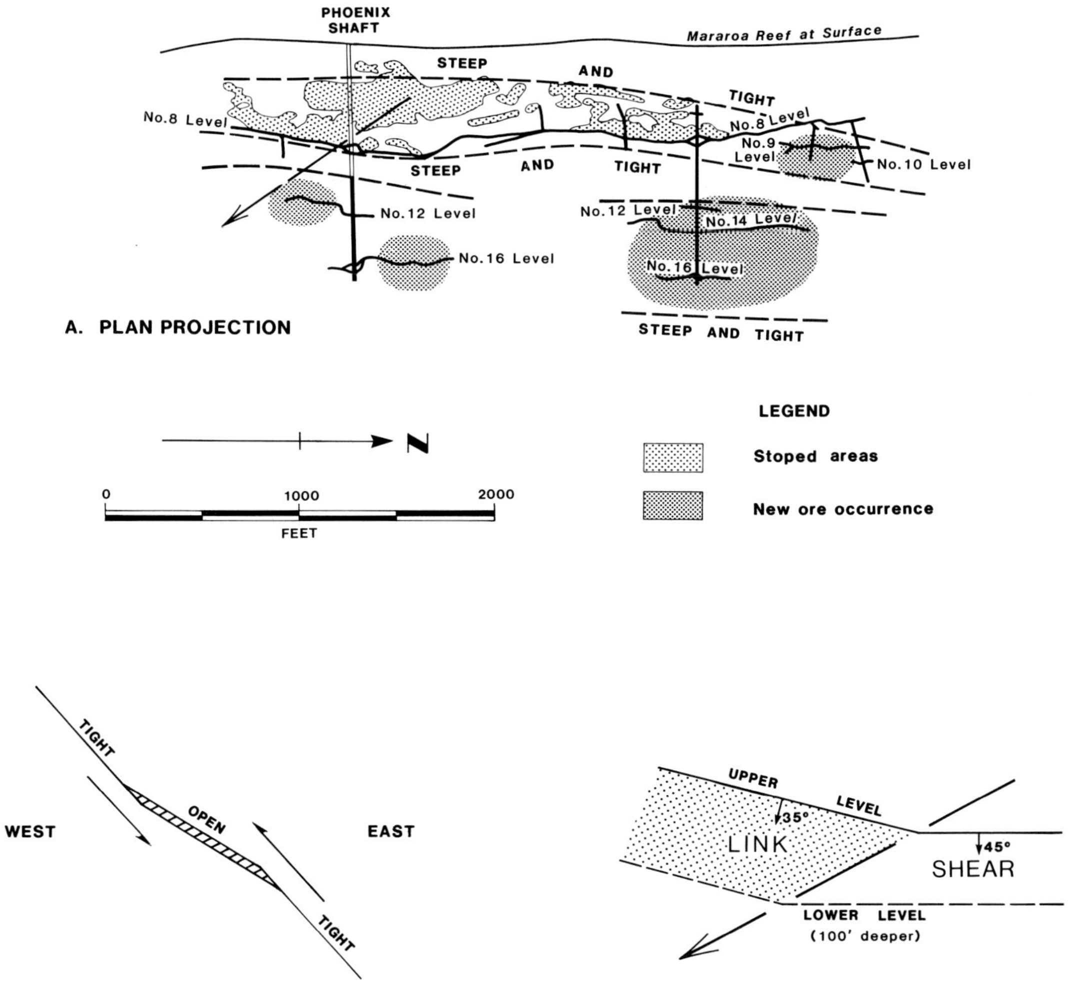

Figure 9 Geological concepts arising during 1938.

A. Plan projection of the Mararoa reef showing the alternation of steeply-dipping and flatly-dipping sections of the reef. The suspected over-all south pitch of ore occurrence is shown by the arrow.

B. Sketch cross section looking north showing that, under the influence of a shearing couple, the flatter dipping section would be more open.

C. Plan projection of a hypothetical shear-link intersection where the link trends to the east of north. The pitch of the intersection is to the south, as is indicated by the arrow.

Figure 9

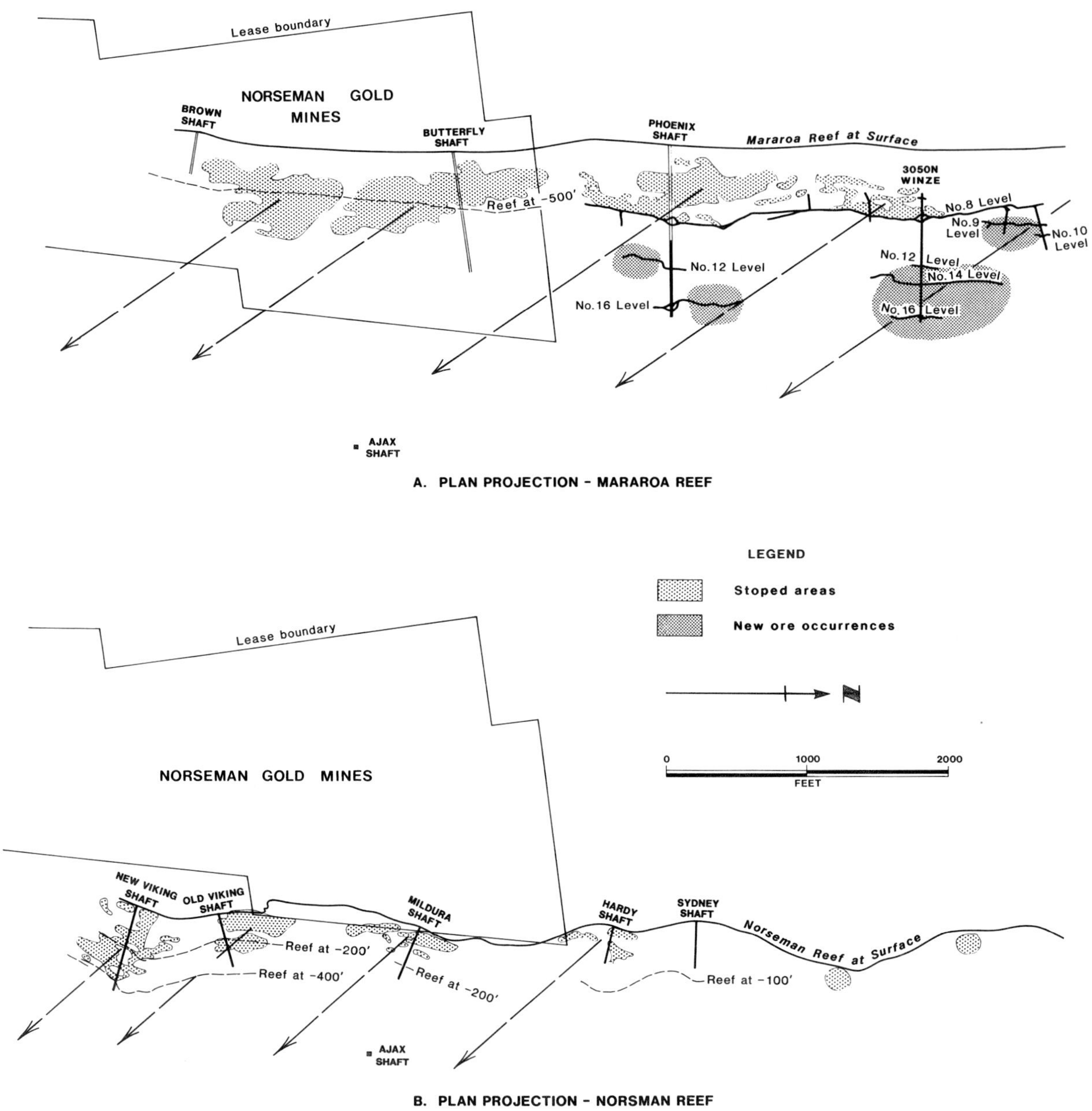

Figure 10

Figure 10 **The Ajax shaft concept.**
There was thought to be a south-pitching ore control, indicated by the arrows, yielding ore bodies in depth within a succession of horizontally-disposed favourable zones — see Figure 9A.

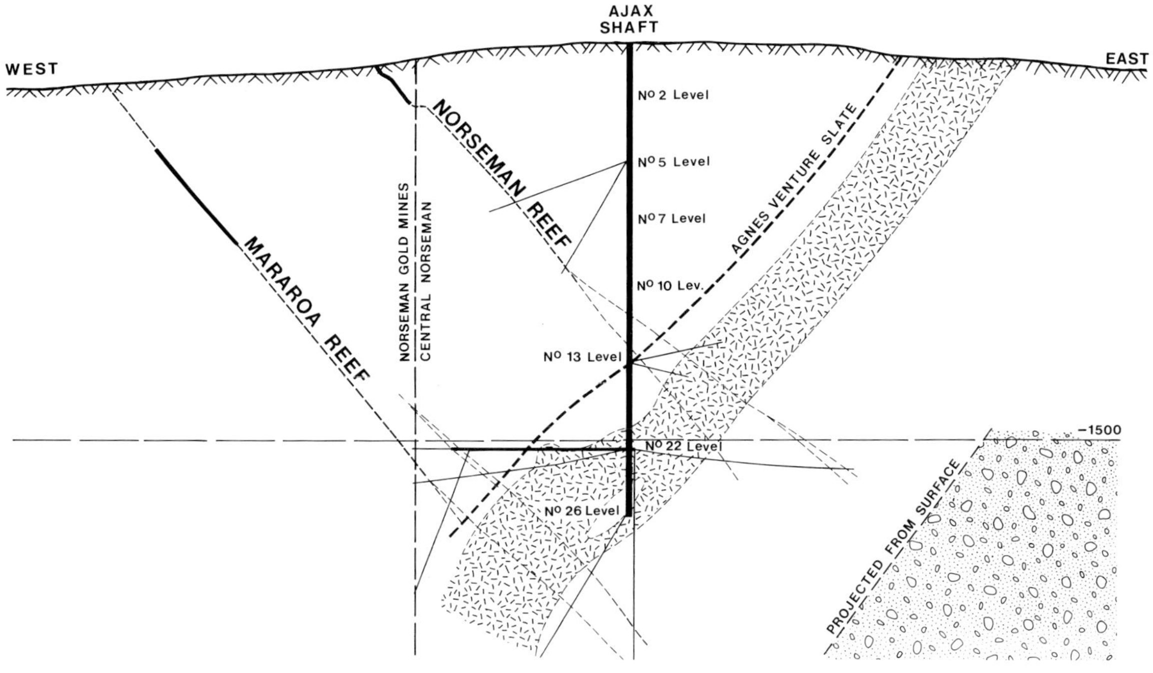

A. AJAX SHAFT

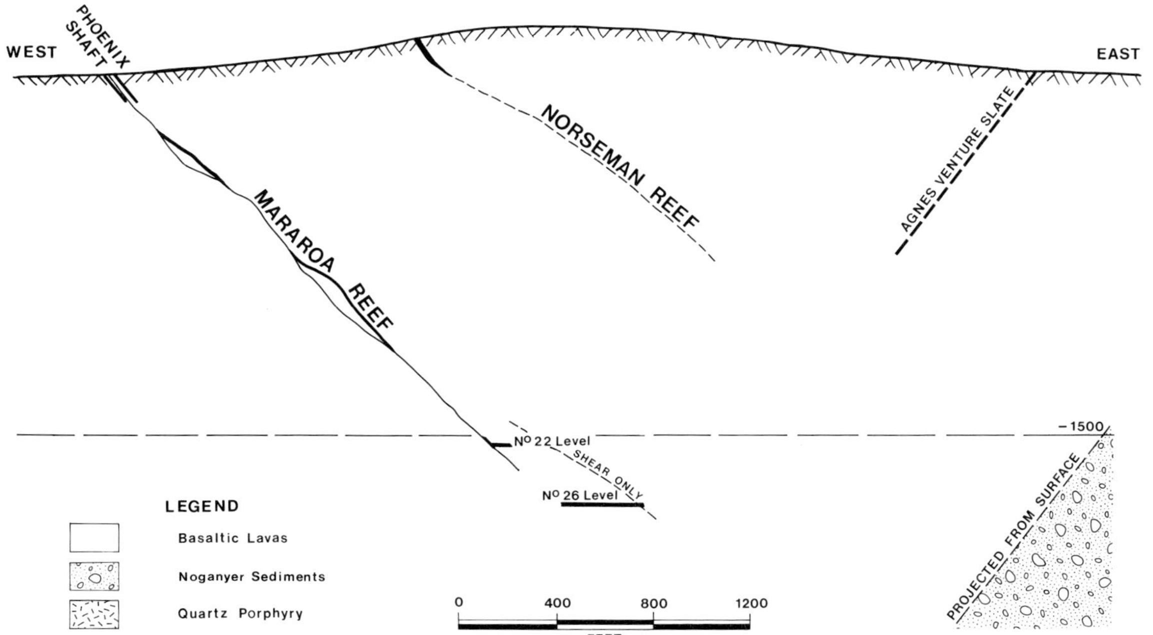

B. PHOENIX SHAFT

Figure 11 Cross sections, looking north.

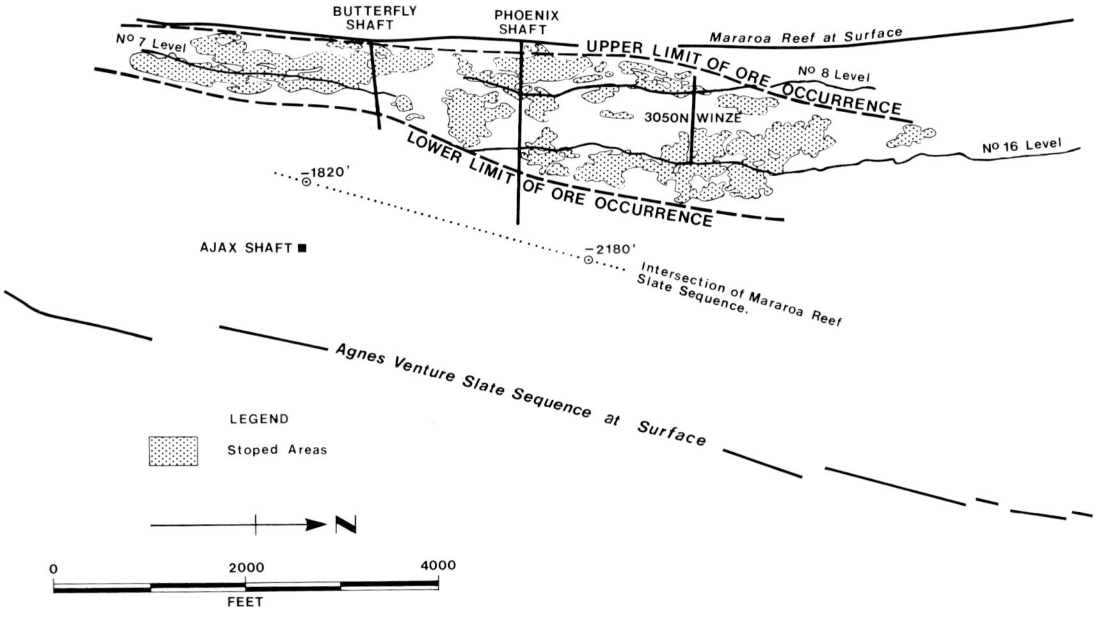

Figure 12

Figure 12 Plan projection showing the relationship between ore occurrence on the Mararoa reef and the surface trend of the Agnes Venture slate sequence.

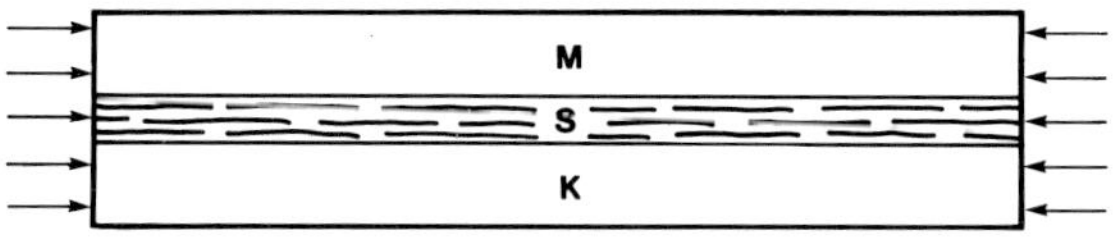

A.

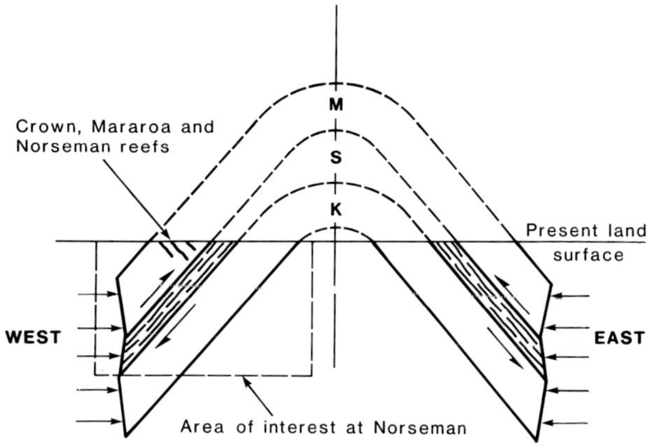

B.

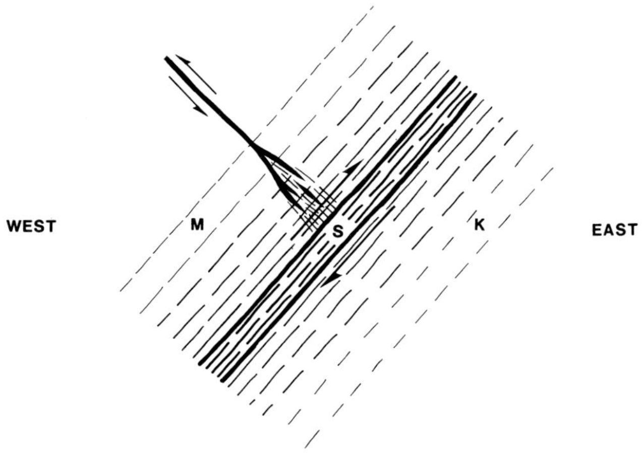

C.

Figure 13 Cross sections looking north, giving an analysis of the effect on reef fracturing of a slate band involved in regional folding.
Figure 13B indicates the area of interest and suggests the scale of the reefs in relation to their geological setting.

Figure 13

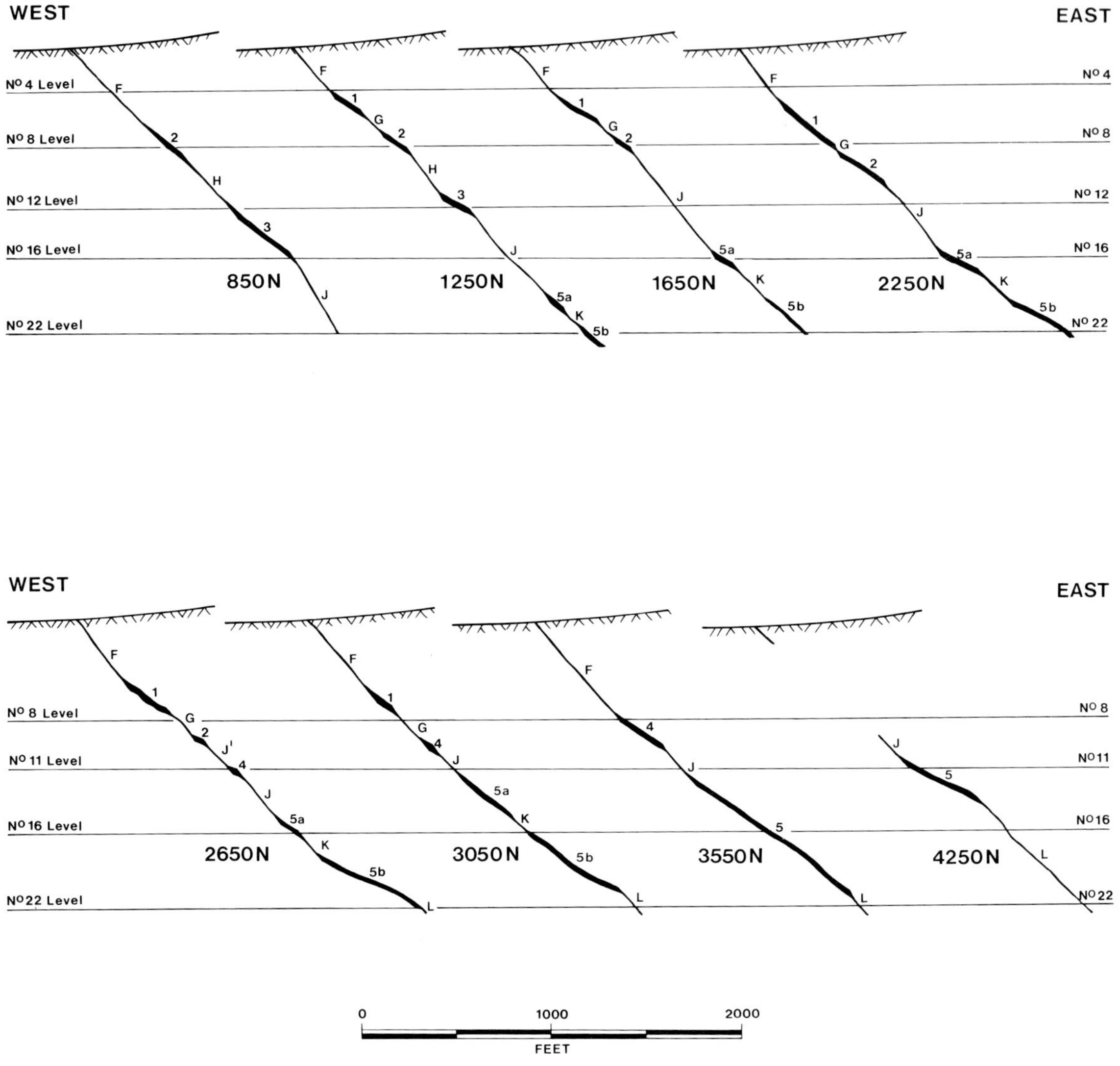

Figure 14

Figure 14 Cross sections of the Mararoa reef looking north. The section lines are shown in Plate 3. Shears indicated by letters and links by numbers. Quartz thicknesses on the links are exaggerated to help presentation.

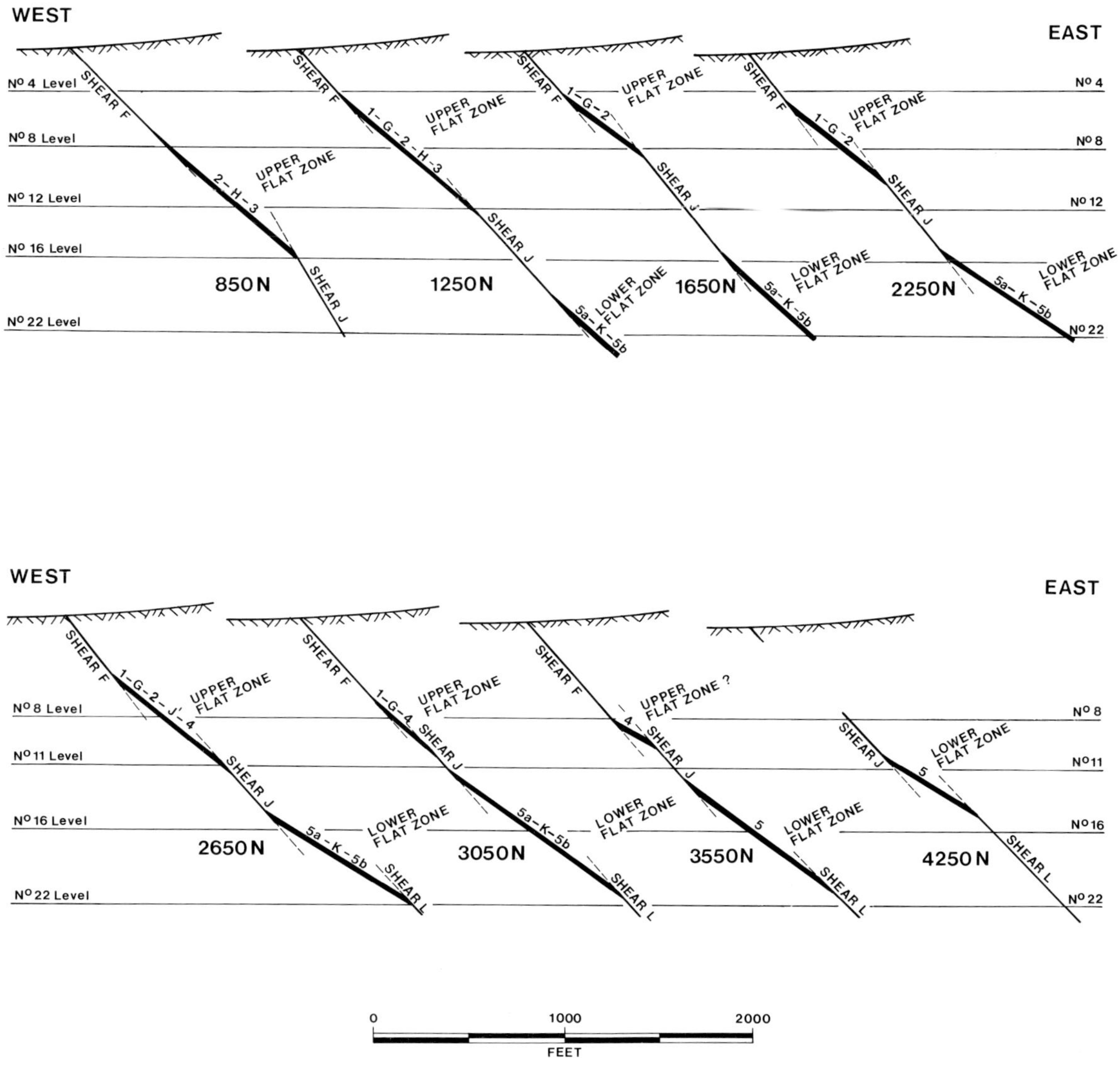

Figure 15 The cross sections of Figure 14 repeated in generalised form. There are three dominant shears — F, J and L. The lesser shears and the links are grouped into upper and lower flat zones presented at their average dips. The lightly dashed extensions of the dominant shears are for emphasis only.

Figure 15

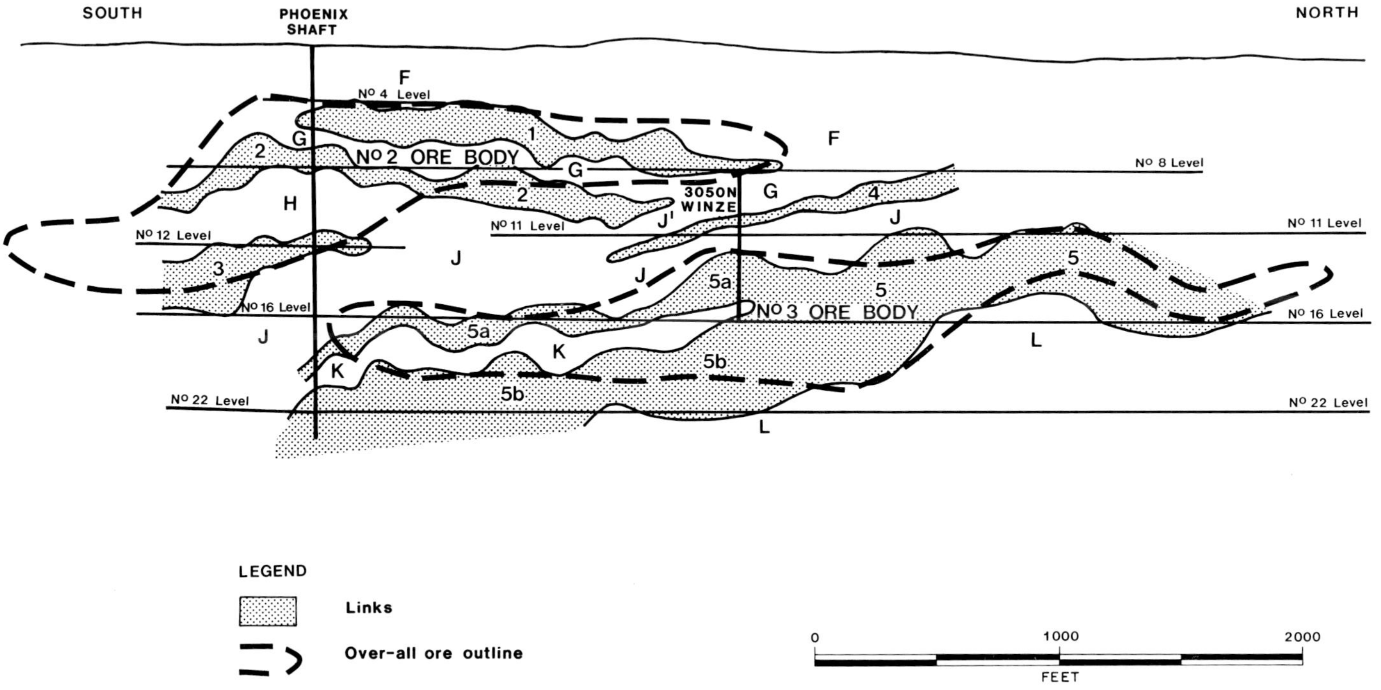

Figure 16

Figure 16 Longitudinal projection of Mararoa reef showing the S structures of the No. 2 and No. 3 ore bodies.

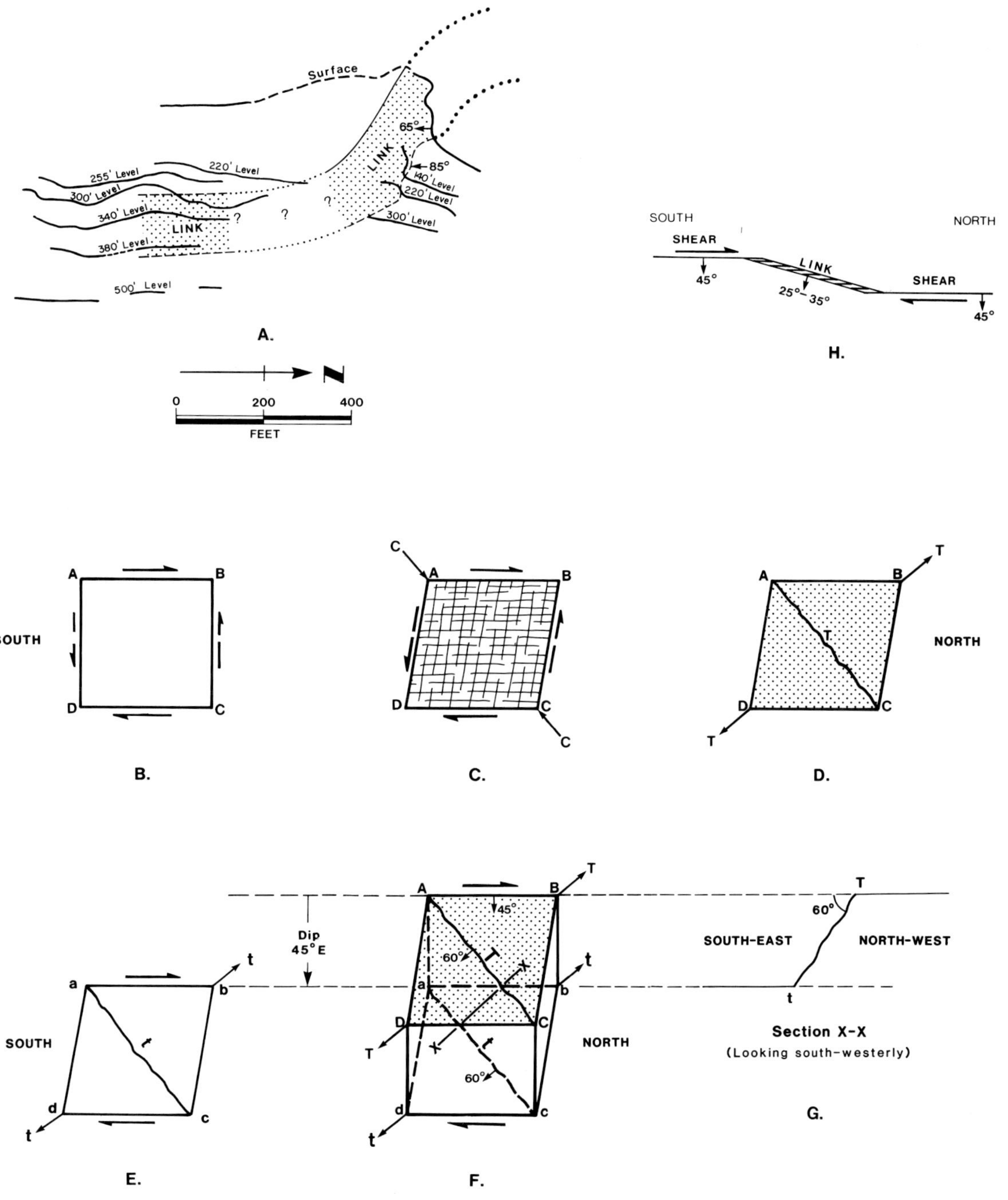

Figure 17

Figure 17 A. Plan projection of old Princess Royal mine showing its S structure.
B.-G. Analysis of fracturing, described in text.
H. Plan view of a shear-link intersection. The shearing movement causes the link to be relatively more open than the shears.

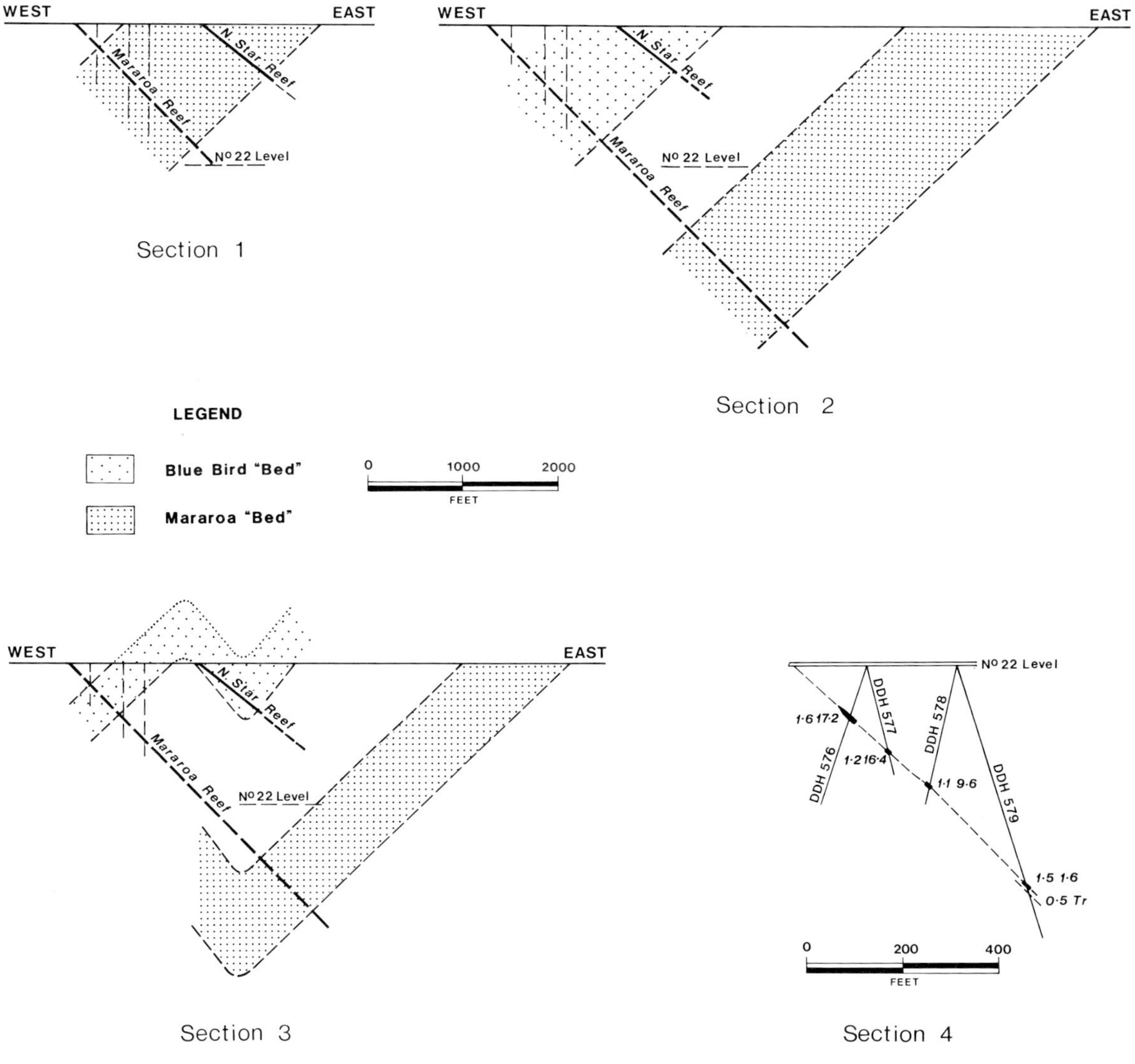

Figure 18

Figure 18 Cross sections looking north.
1. At 7350N showing alternative AA, Plate 5B.
2. At 7350N showing alternative BB, Plate 5B.
3. At 7350N showing the folding hypothesis of Plate 6A.
4. Showing the results of the diamond drilling from 6025N cross cut.

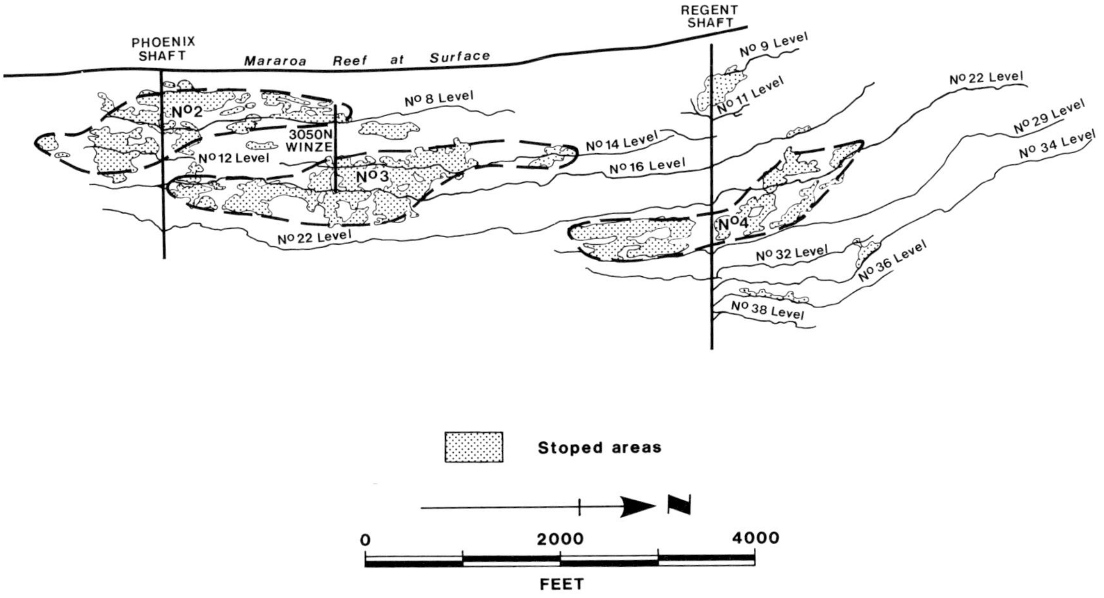

Figure 19 Plan projection showing the deep development at the northern end of the Mararoa reef.

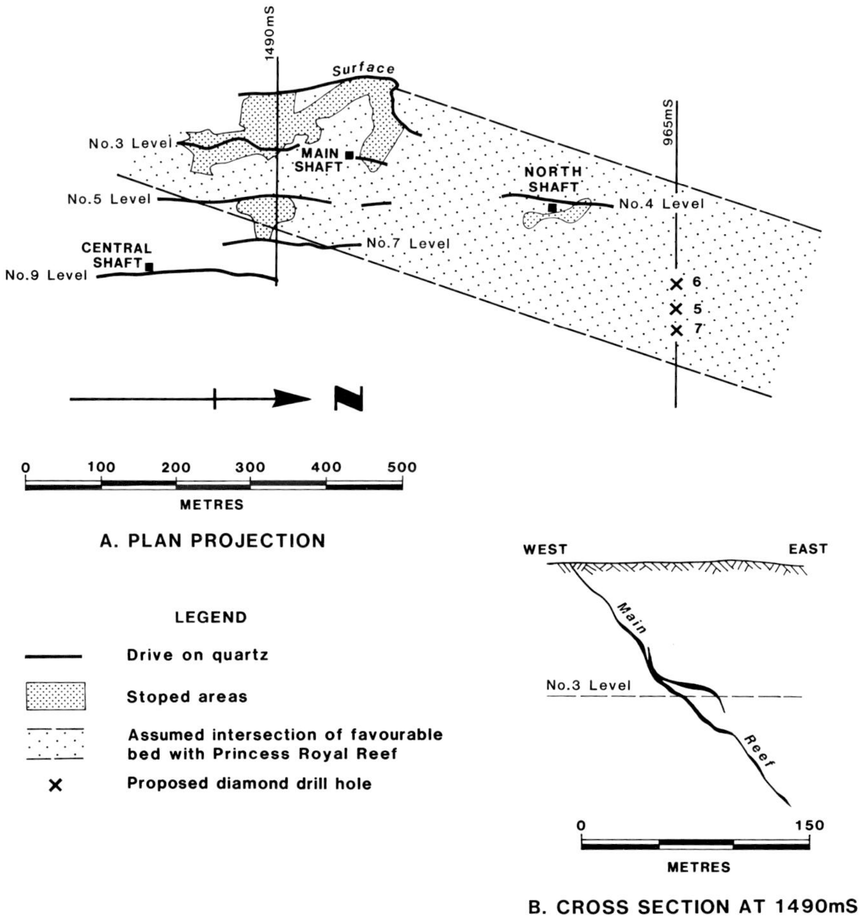

Figure 20 A. Plan projection — reconstruction of Haddon King's layout of diamond drill holes PRS 5, 6 and 7 on the Princess Royal reef.

B. Cross section looking north at 1490mS, after W.D. Campbell, 1906, G.S.W.A. Bulletin No. 21.

Figure 20

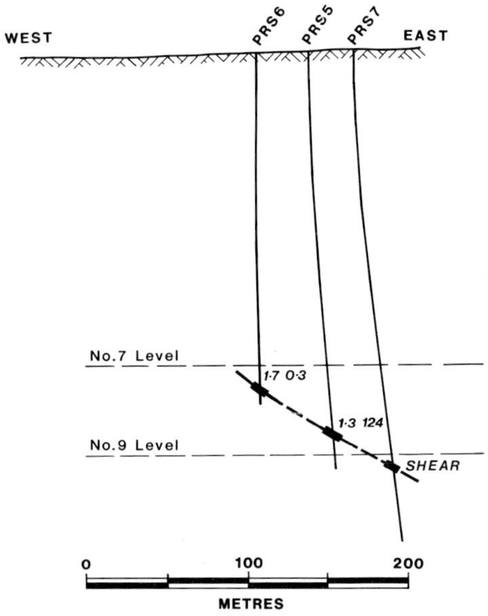

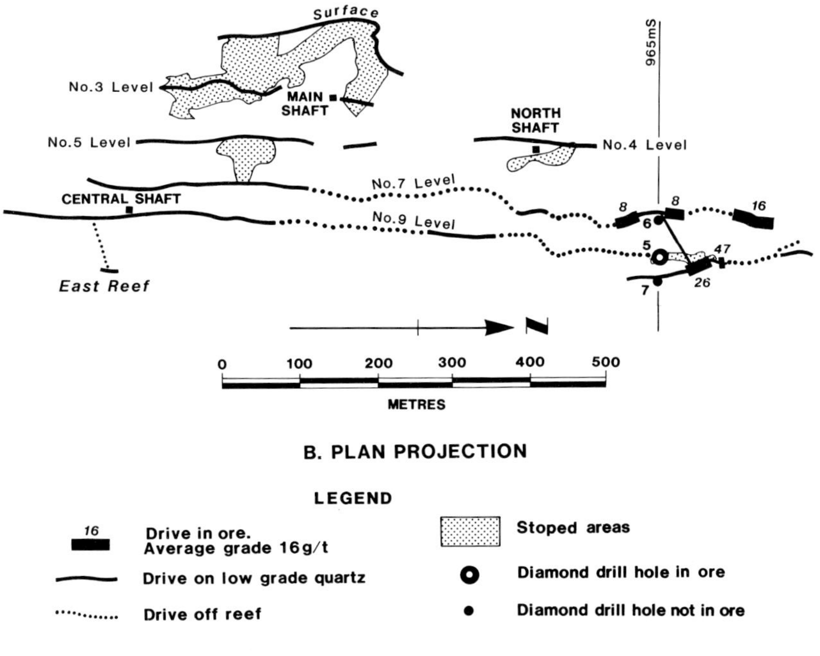

Figure 21 A. Cross section looking north showing reef intersections in diamond drill holes PRS 5, 6 and 7.
B. Plan projection showing development results on the Princess Royal reef to December 1946.

Figure 21

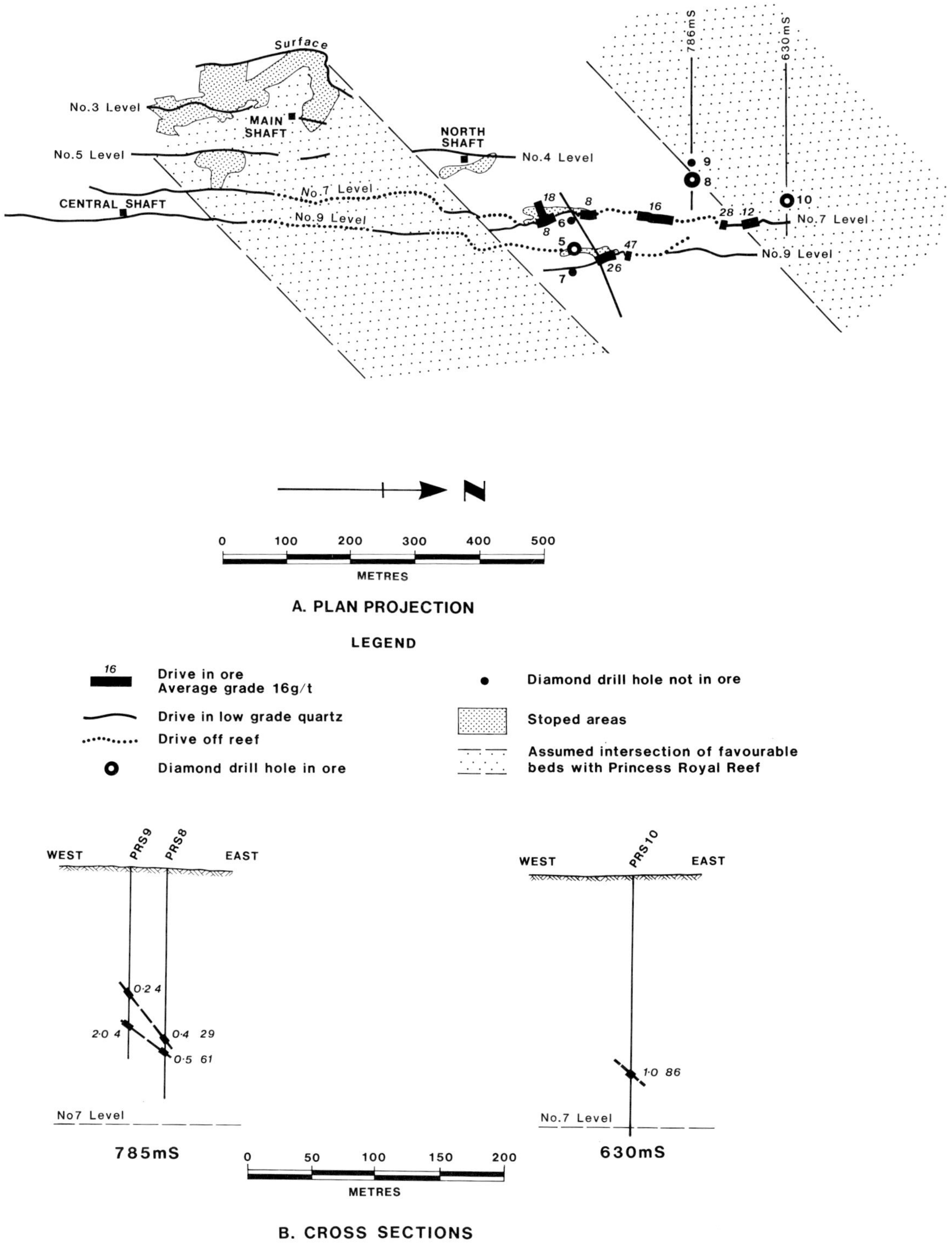

Figure 22

Figure 22 A. Plan projection showing development and diamond drilling results on the Princess Royal reef to November 1947 and their relationship to the postulated favourable beds.
B. Cross sections looking north showing reef intersections in diamond drill holes PRS 8, 9 and 10.

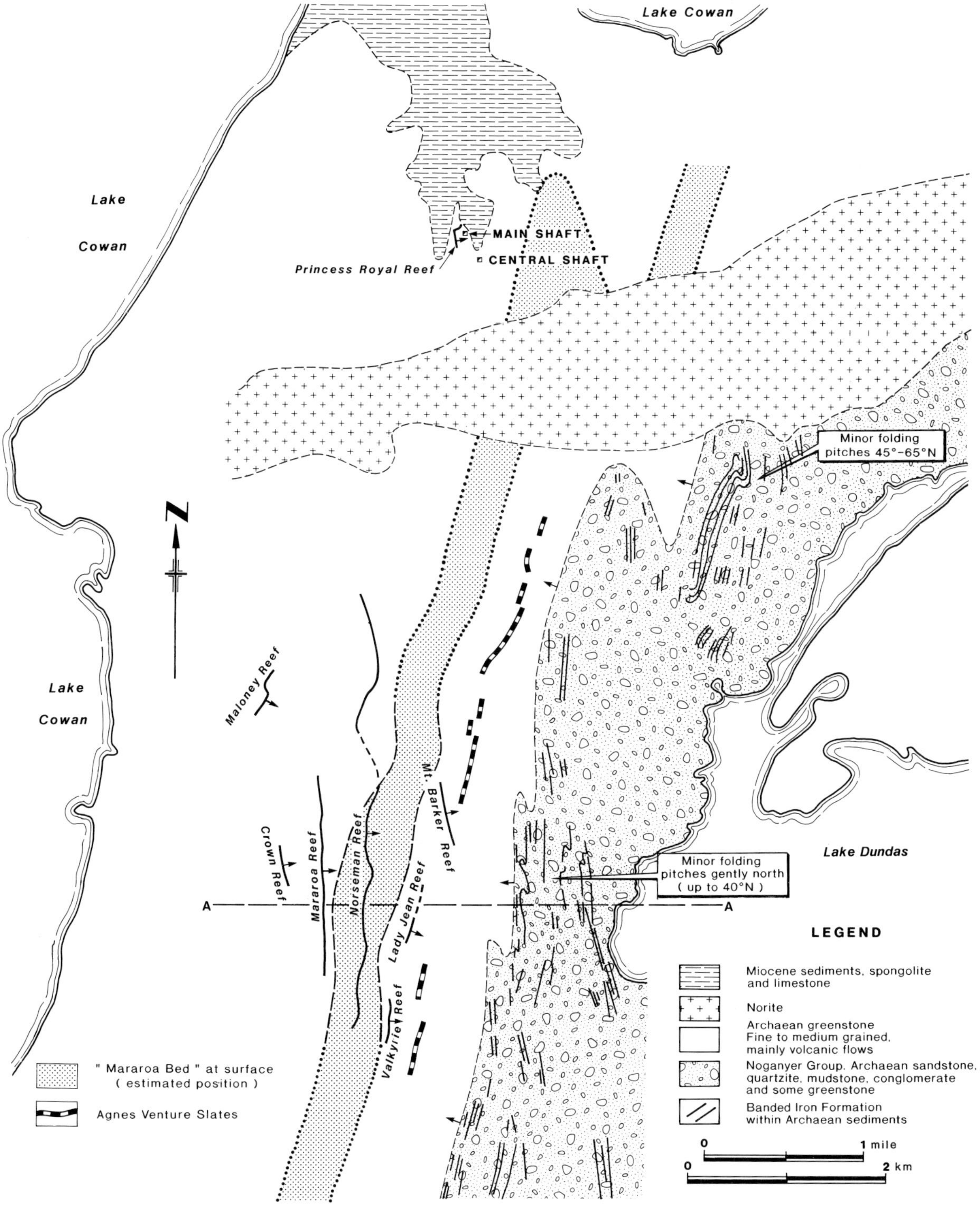

Figure 23 Surface geological map — Figure 1 repeated, with the addition of the Agnes Venture slate sequence and the Mararoa "favourable bed". The dashed line limits for the Mararoa bed are derived from underground data; the dotted lines are extrapolations parallel to geological trends.

Figure 23

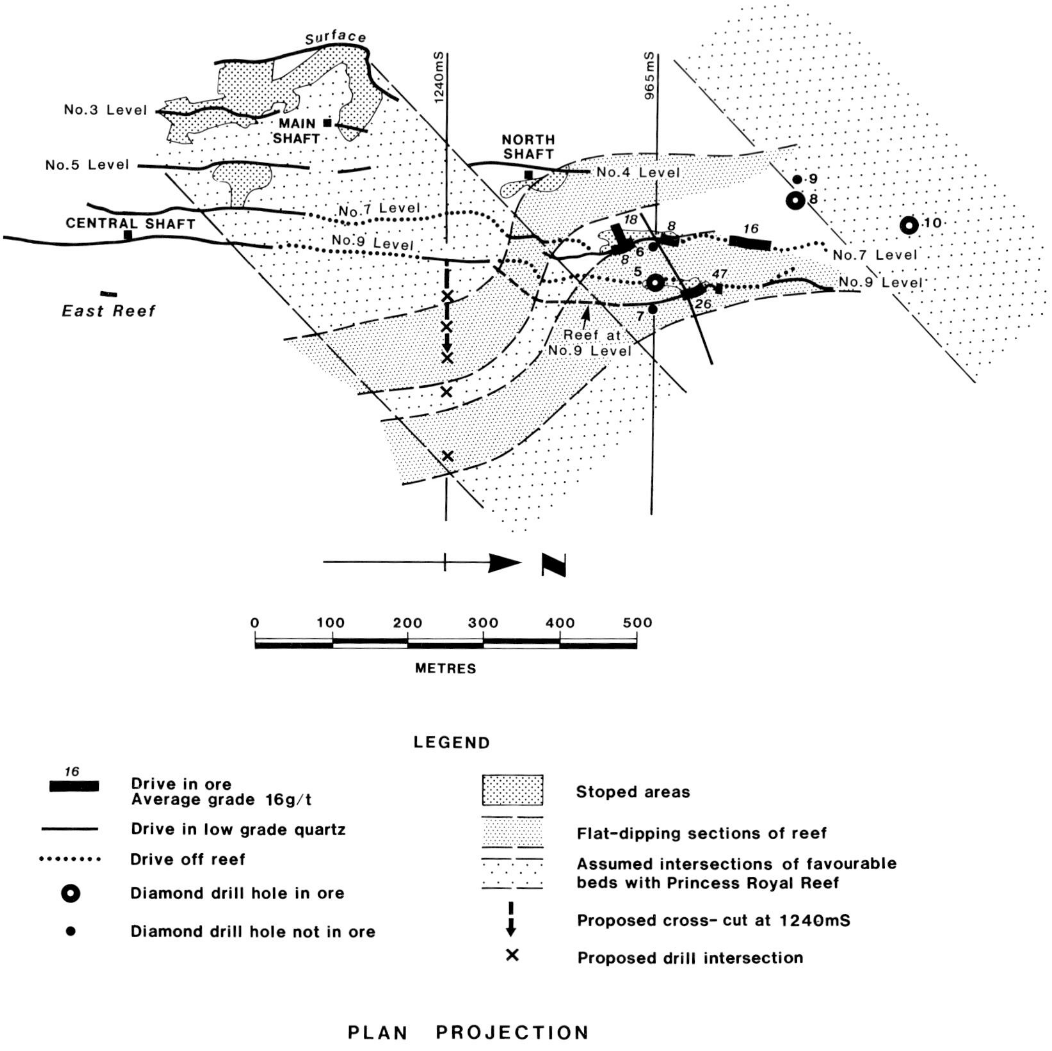

Figure 24

Figure 24 Plan projection of the Princess Royal reef showing structural concepts by J.D. Campbell and D. O'Driscoll, 19/11/1947, Report K/716.

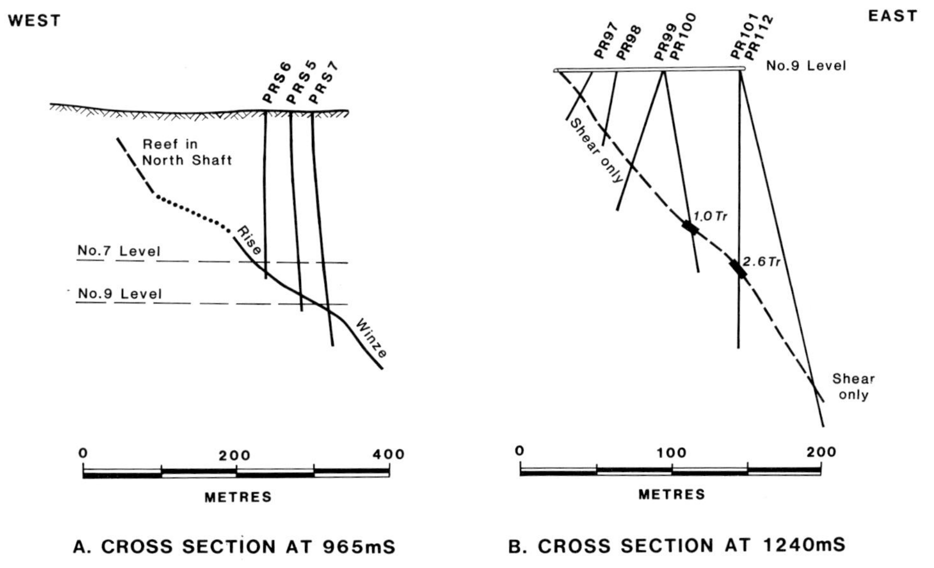

Figure 25 Cross sections looking north relating to Figure 24.
A. Known and suspected steeply and flatly dipping sections of the reef.
B. Reef intersections in the diamond drilling below No. 9 level.

Figure 25

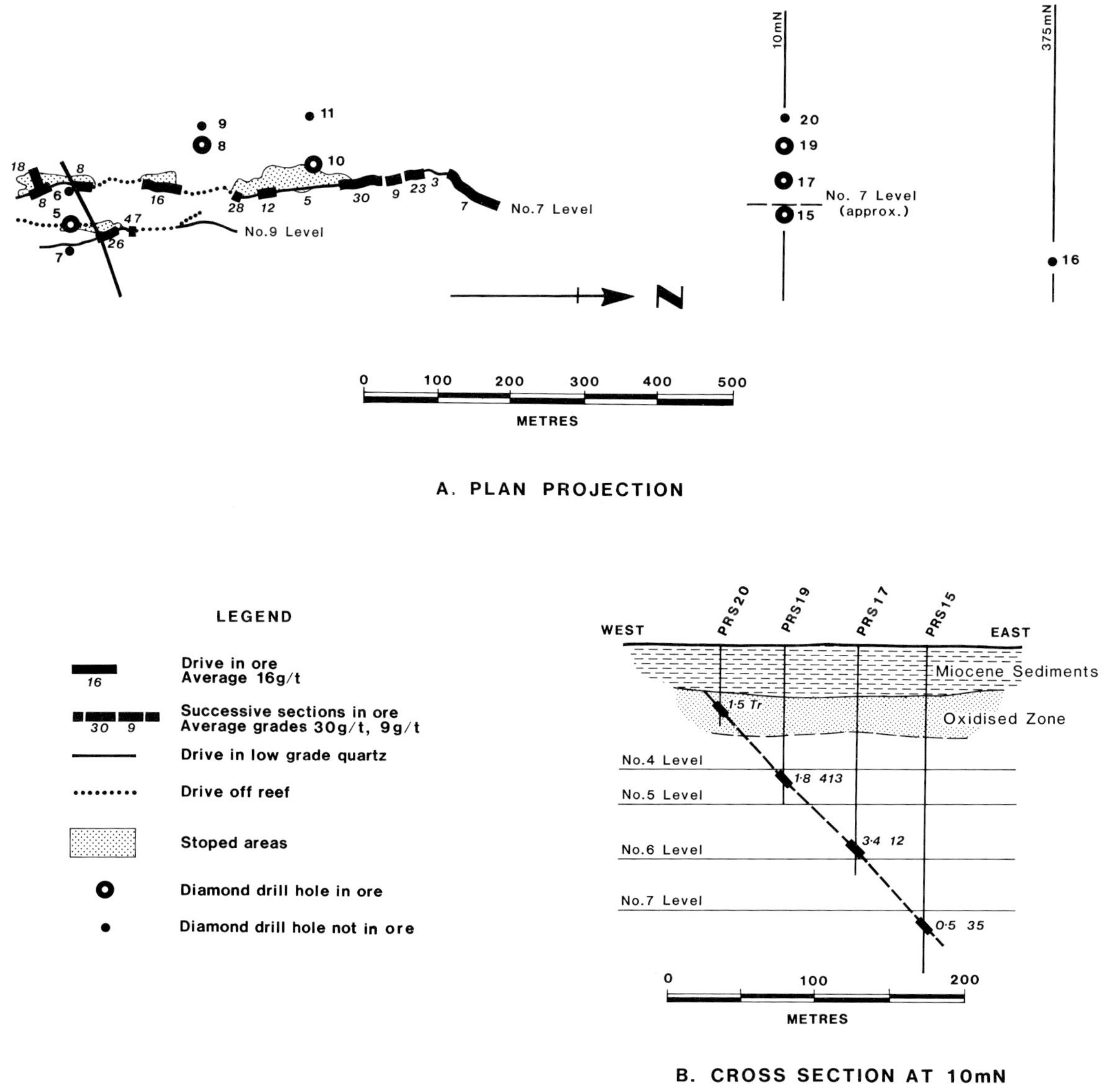

Figure 26 A. Plan projection showing development and diamond drilling results on the Princess Royal reef to December 1949.
Over-all, the ore indications are parallel to No. 7 level.
B. Cross section looking north showing the reef intersections in diamond drill holes PRS 15, 17, 19 and 20.

Figure 26

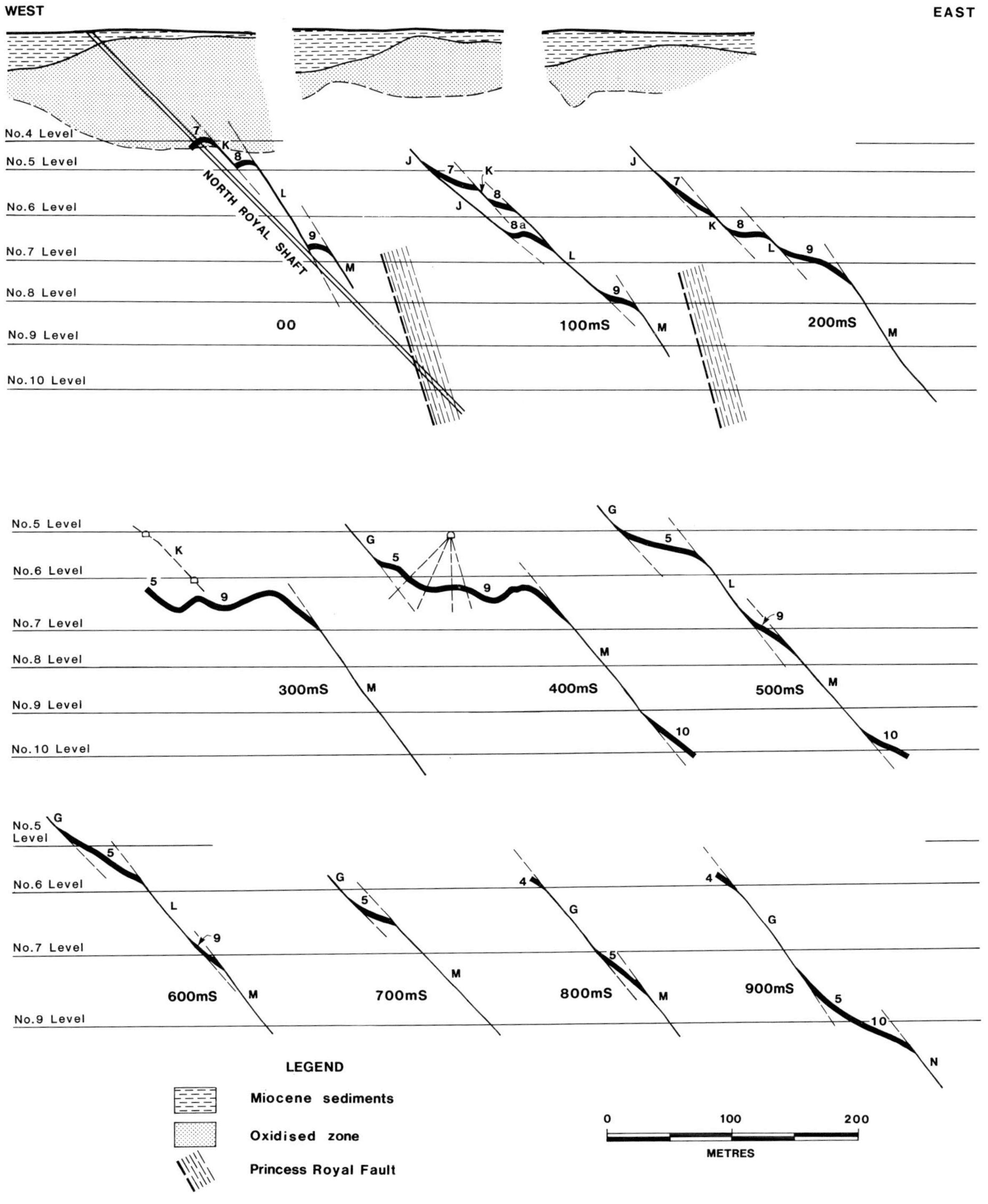

Figure 27 Cross sections looking north at intervals of 100m from 900mS to the North Royal shaft showing the shear-link pattern of the Princess Royal reef — see Plate 8 for locations. Note: the dashed line extensions of the shears are for emphasis only; they do not indicate a continuation of the reef. The width of the quartz on the links has been exaggerated.

Figure 27

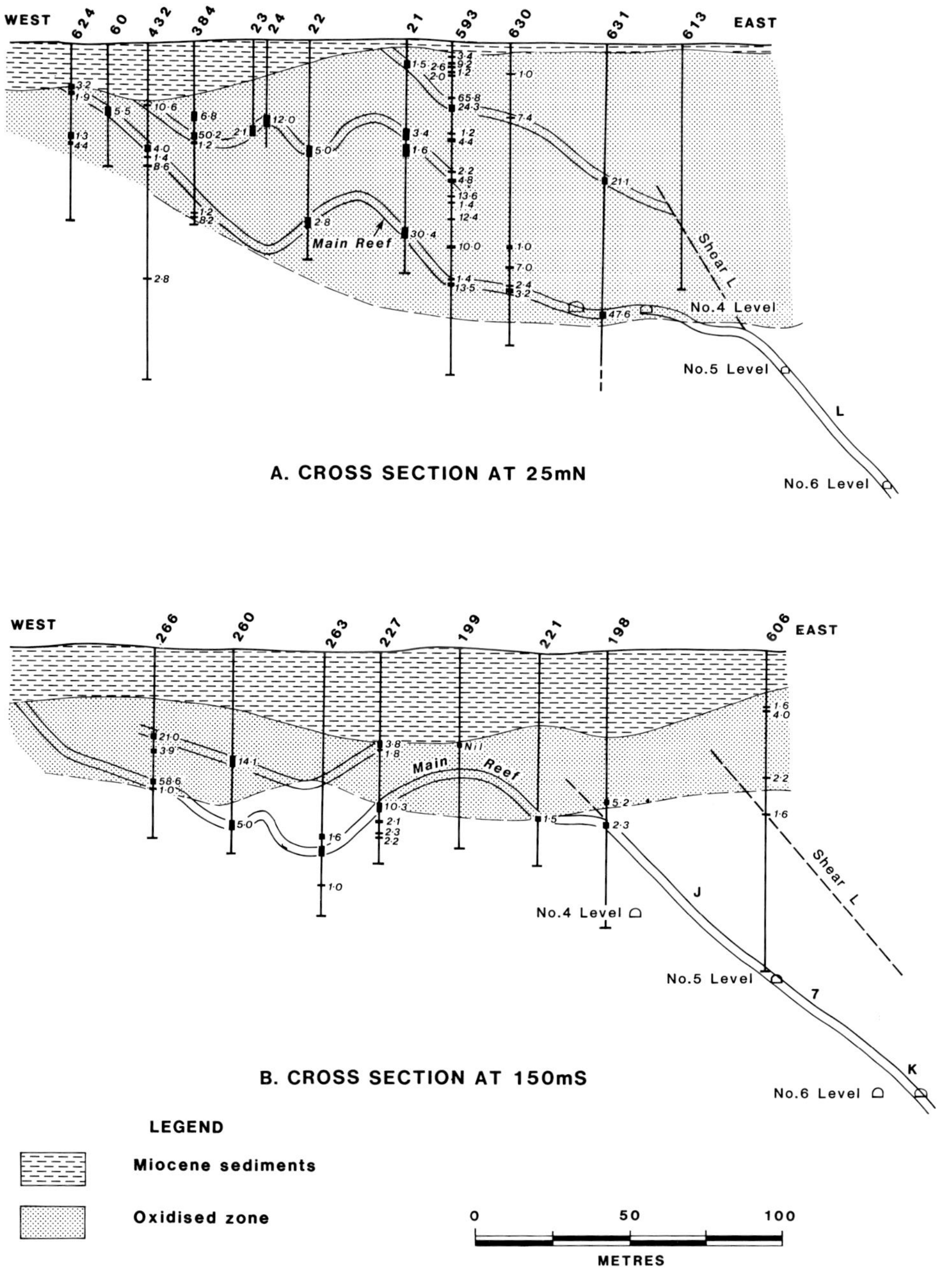

Figure 28

Figure 28 Cross sections of the Princess Royal reef looking north showing near surface drilling and assay results.

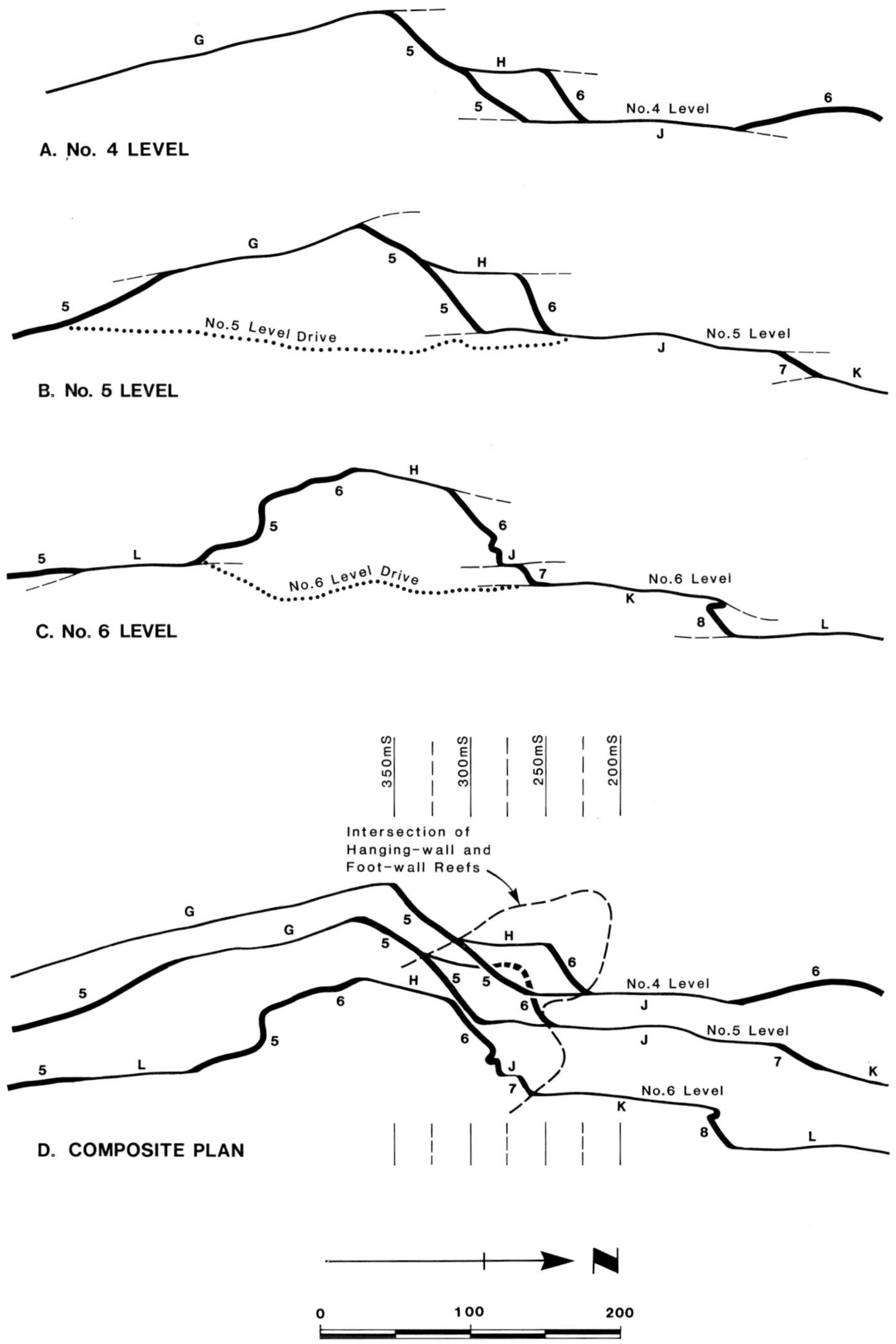

Figure 29 Plans of the interpreted shear-link patterns on the Princess Royal reef at No. 4, No. 5 and No. 6 levels and of their inter-relationship in composite plan.

Figure 29

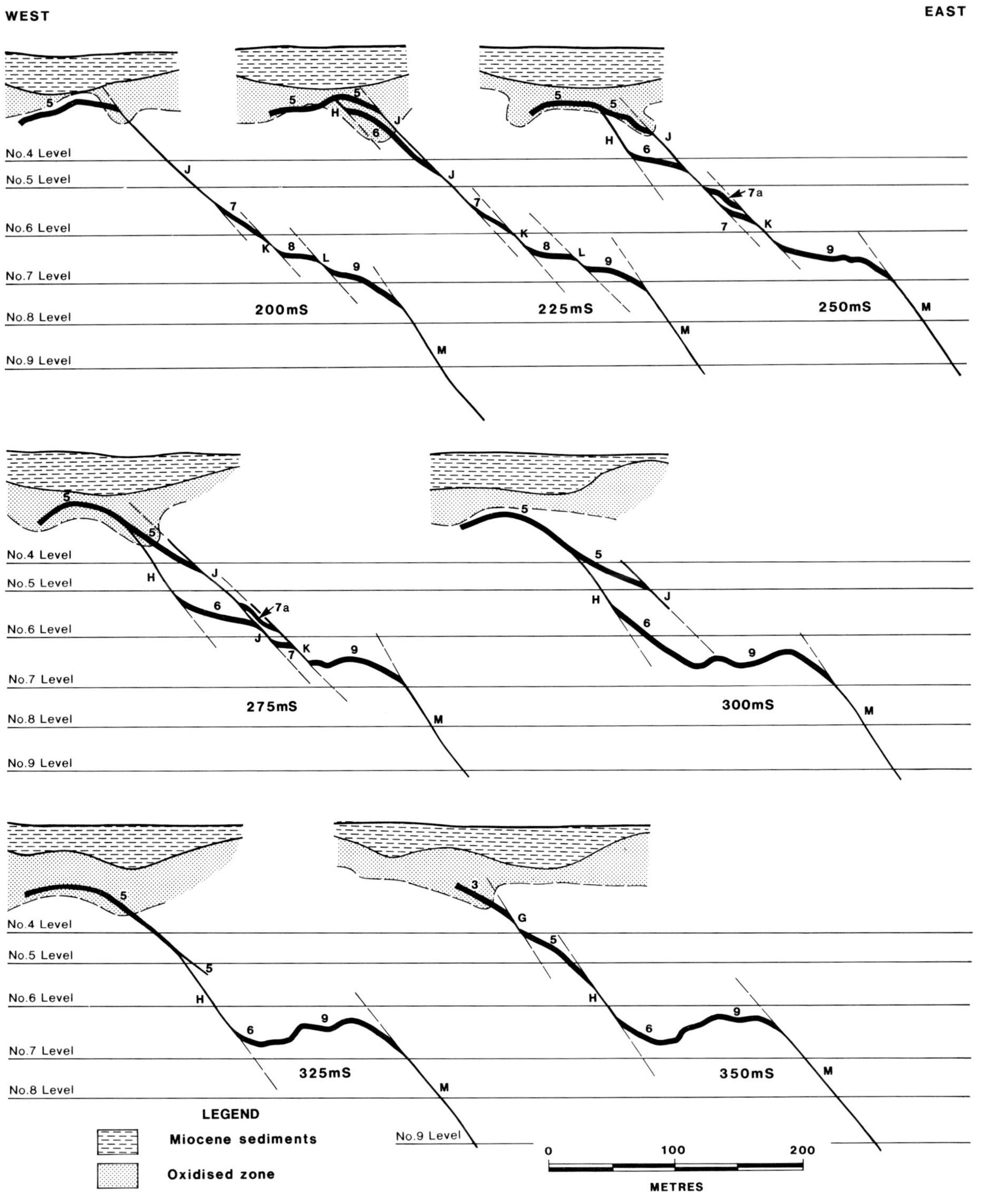

Figure 30

Figure 30 Cross sections of the Princess Royal reef looking north at intervals of 25m through the vein-loop area of Figure 29 showing the interpreted shear-link pattern.

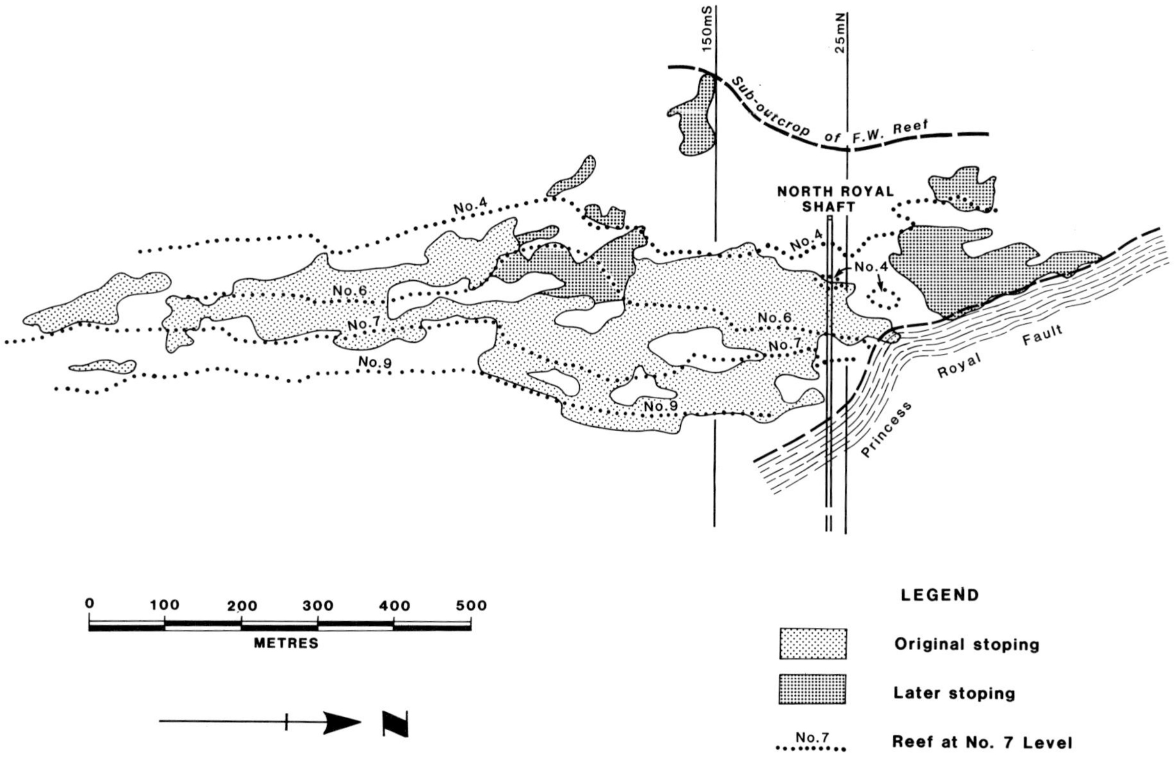

Figure 31 Plan projection of the Princess Royal reef showing near-surface underground mining in relation to the area mined in the original underground operation.

Figure 31

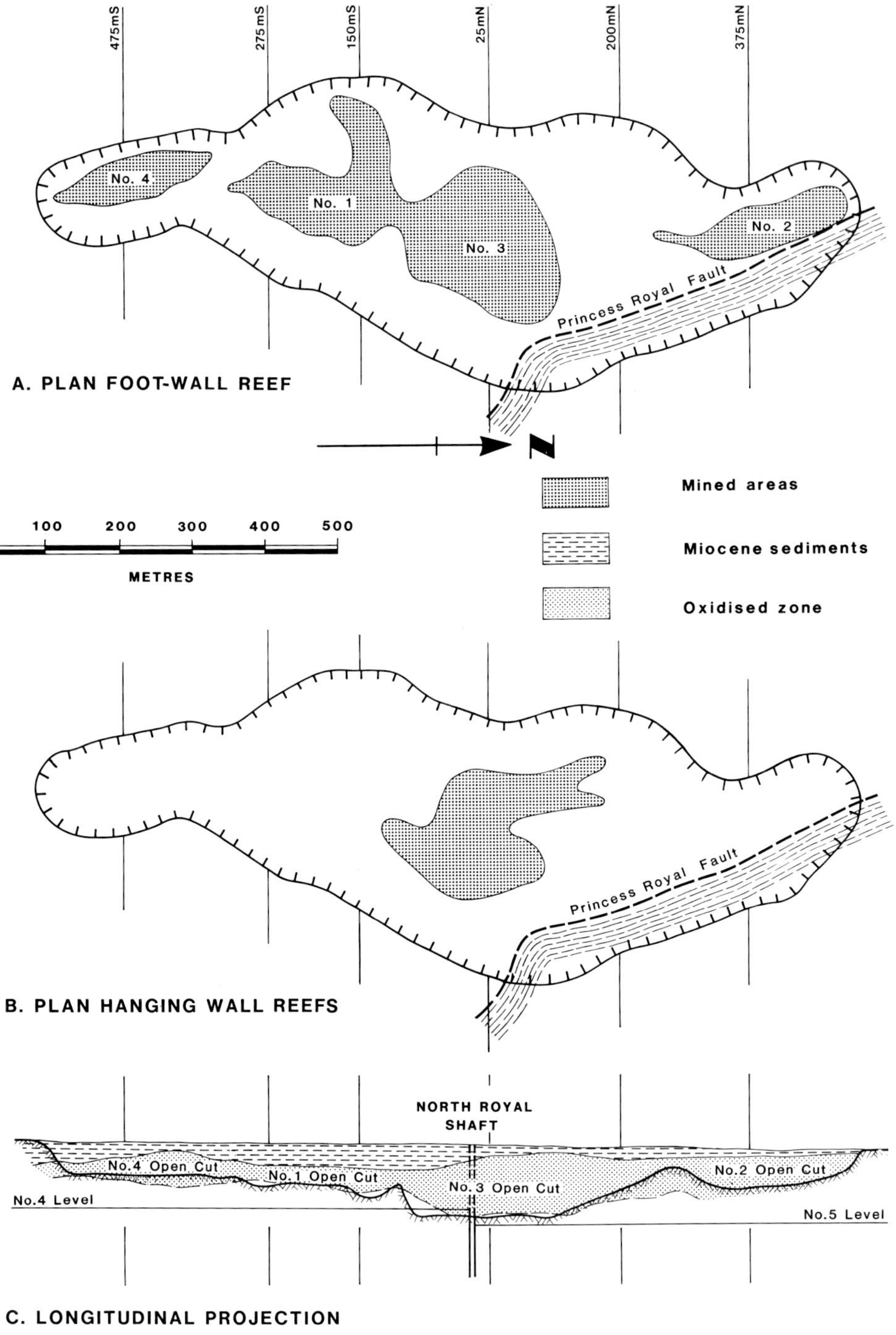

Figure 32

Figure 32 A. and B. Plan projections showing the surface outline of the open-cuts at Princess Royal and the areas of reef mined in them.
C. Longitudinal projection showing the profile of the deepest points reached by the open-cuts.

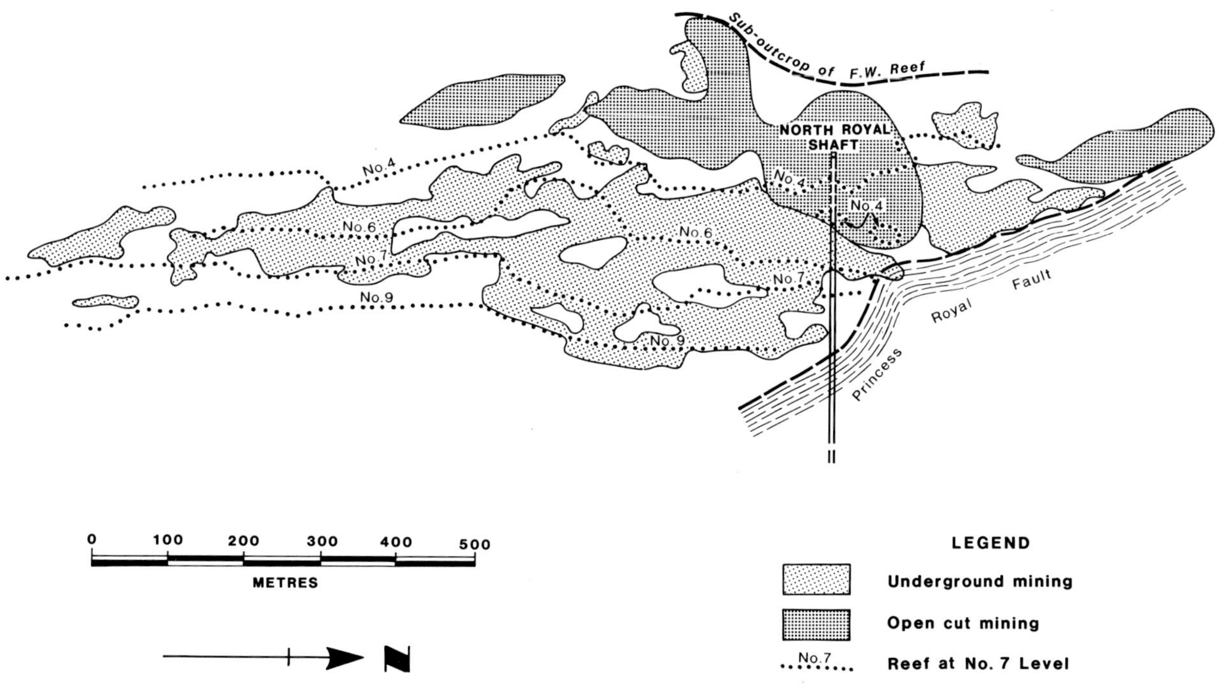

Figure 33 Plan projection showing the areas mined on the foot-wall reef by the underground and open-cut operations at Princess Royal.

Figure 33

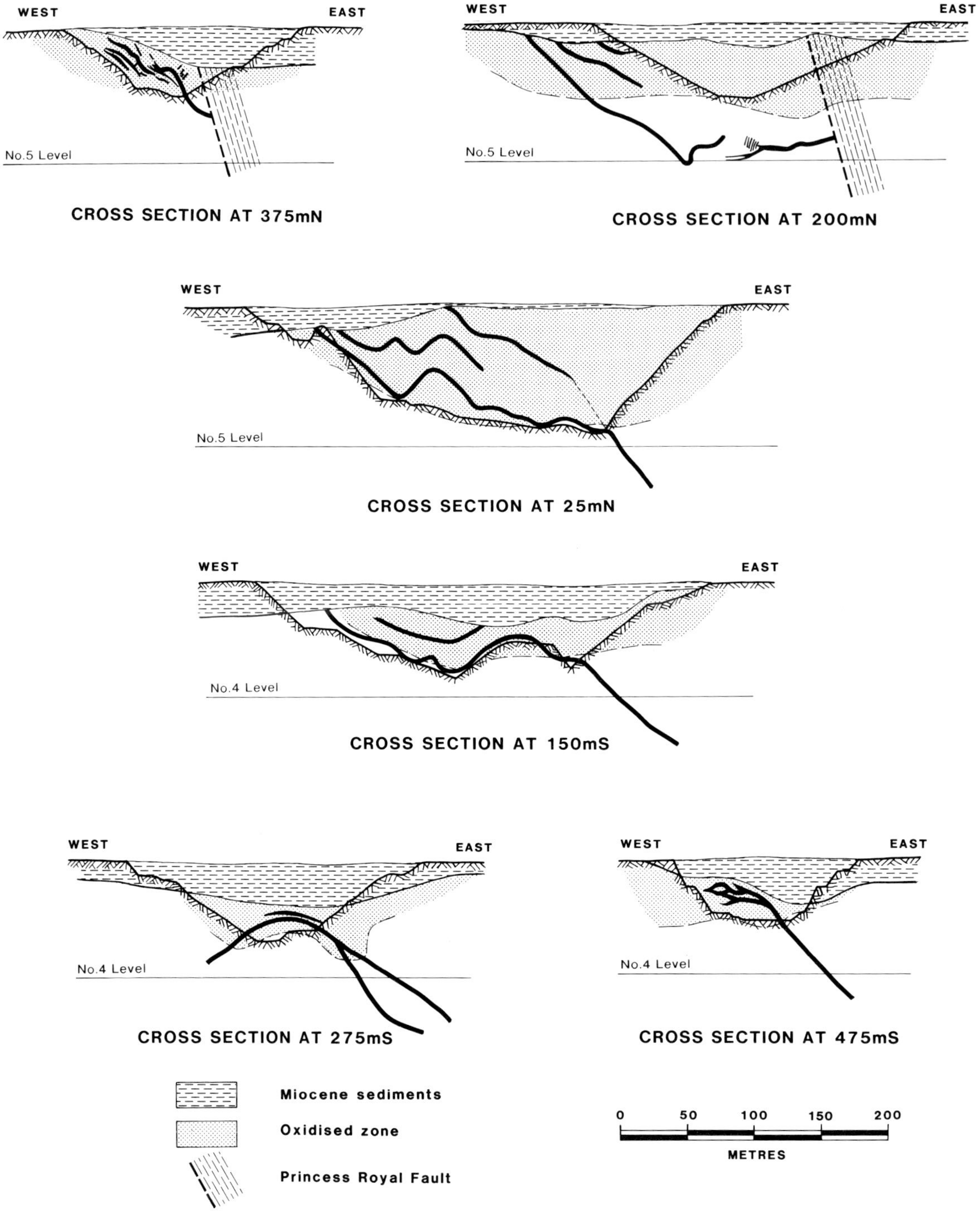

Figure 34

Figure 34 Cross sections looking north showing reef occurrence at Princess Royal in and near the open-cuts (for locations see Figure 32).
Much mining effort was needed in places to remove the Miocene sediments, particularly in the No. 1 Open-cut (see sections 150mS and 275mS).
Most of the foot-wall reef at 200mN was mined from No. 5 level.

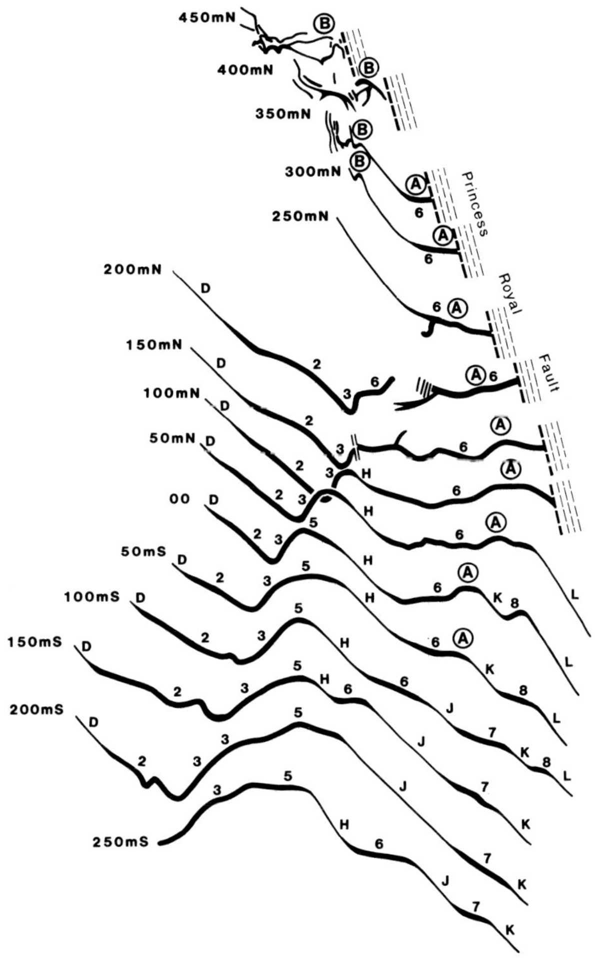

A. STACKED CROSS-SECTIONS

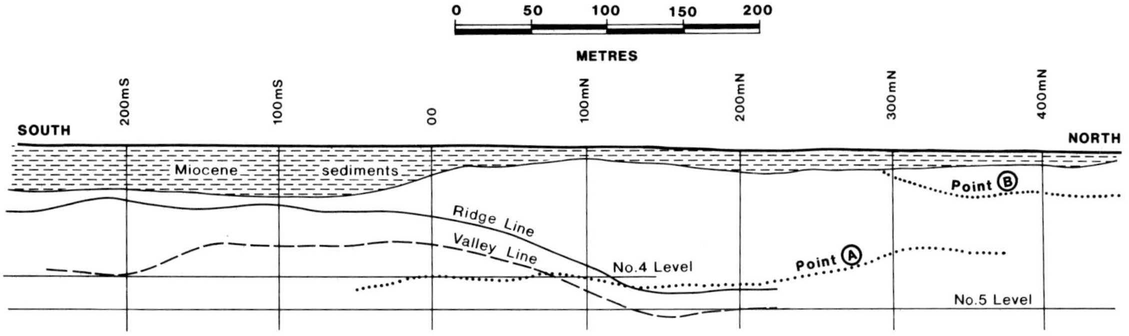

B. LONGITUDINAL PROJECTION

Figure 35 A. "Stacked cross sections" looking north of the foot-wall reef in the near-surface area at Princess Royal.
B. Longitudinal projection showing significant pitch trends.

Figure 35

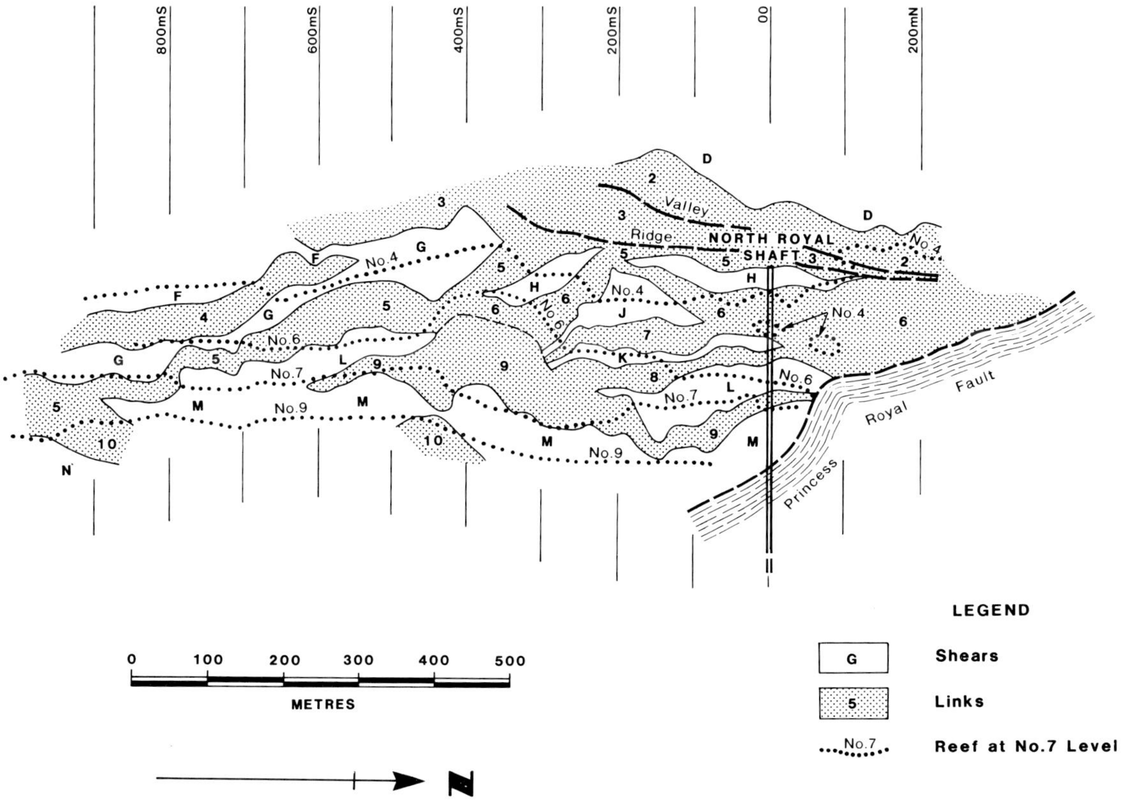

Figure 36

Figure 36 Plan projection showing the shear-link pattern of the foot-wall reef at Princess Royal. Dotted lines show the course of the reef on No. 4, No. 6, No. 7 and No. 9 levels. The reef trend swings to the right when crossing a south-pitching link and to the left when crossing a north-pitching one (e.g. No. 7 level at 200mS).

← Figure 37

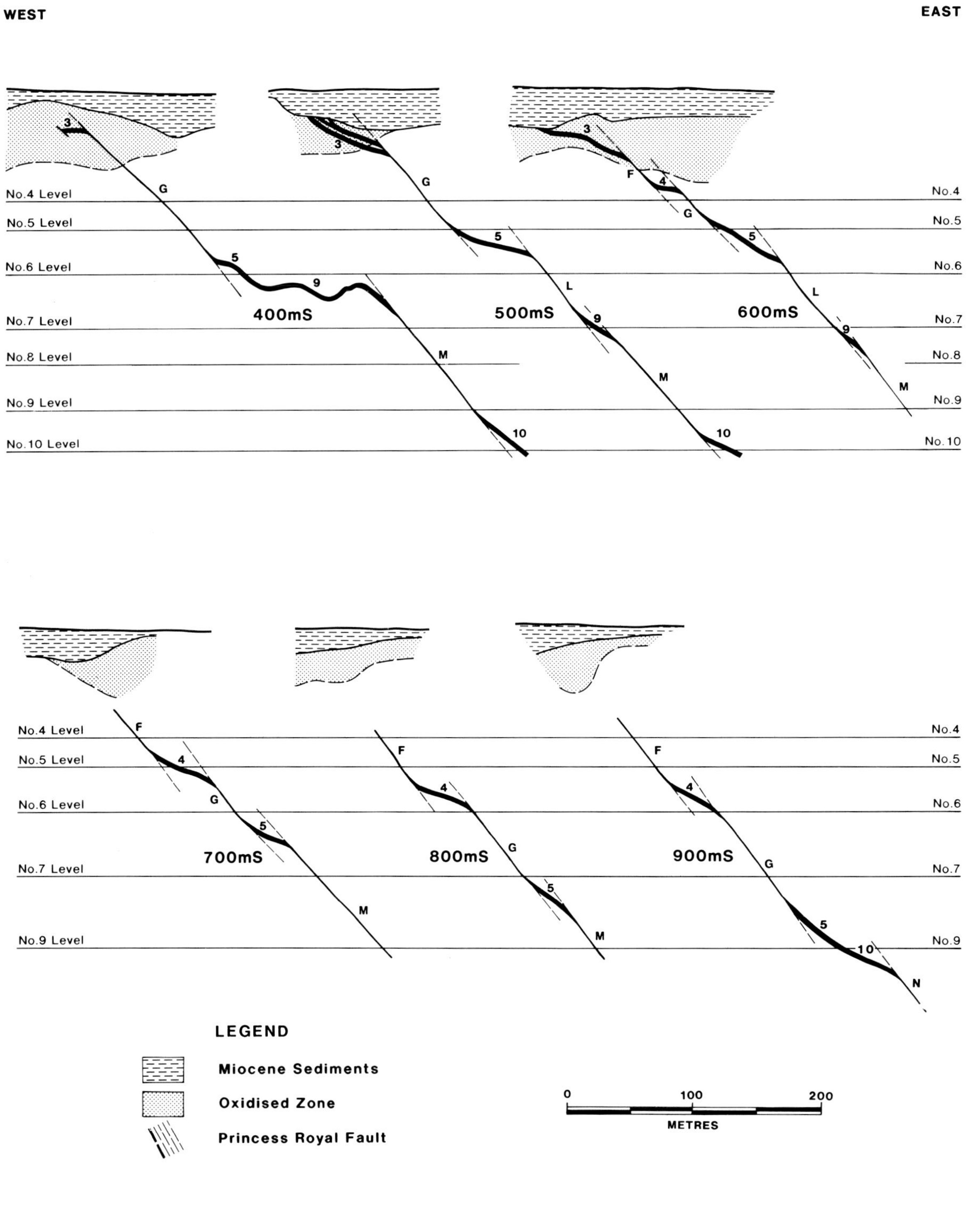

Figure 37 B. Cross sections looking north at 100m intervals for the southern half of the North Royal orebody.

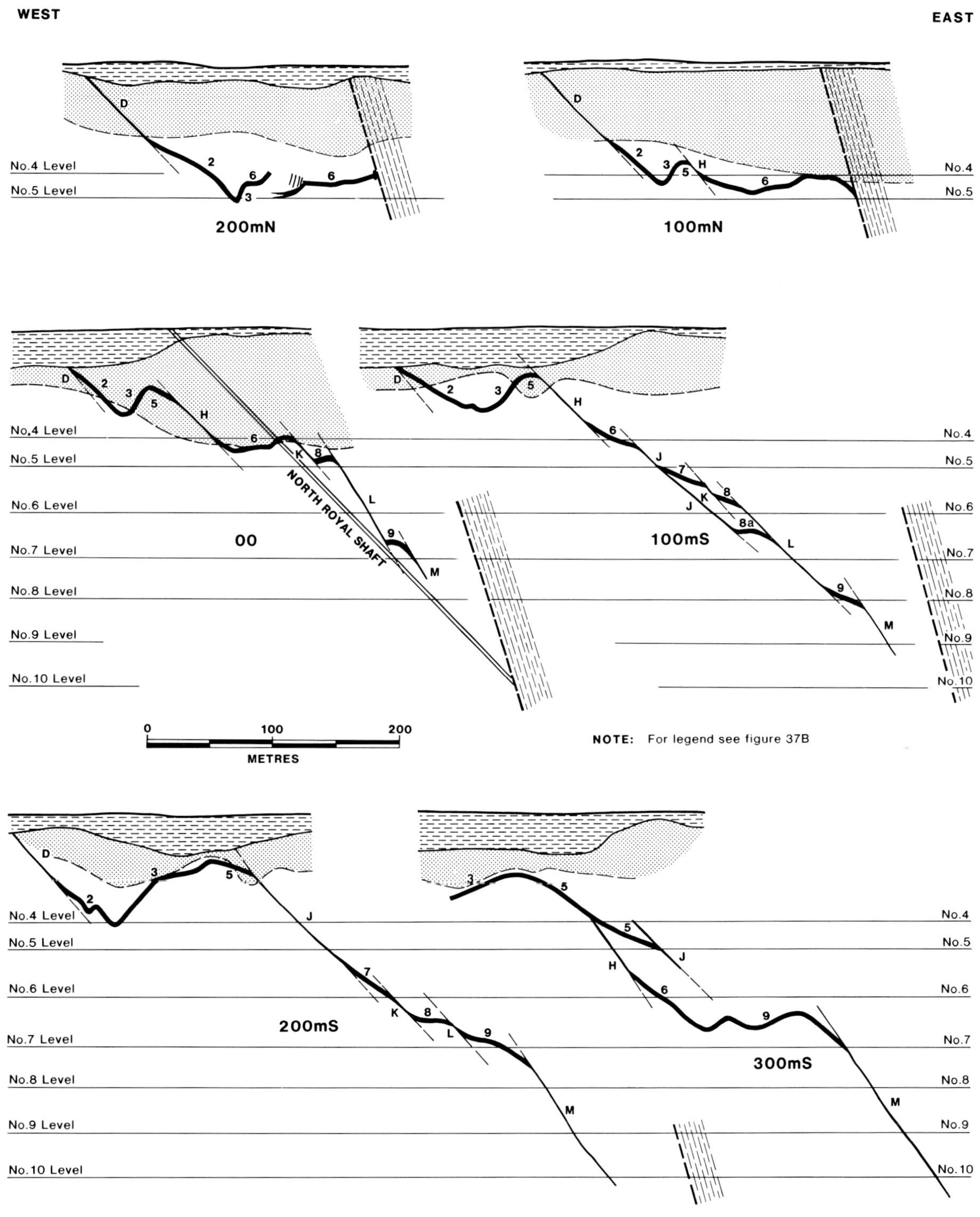

Figure 37 A. **Cross sections of the Princess Royal reef looking north at 100m intervals showing the shear-link pattern of the northern half of the North Royal orebody. The hanging-wall reefs of the open-cuts are not shown as it was not possible to interpret them in detail.**

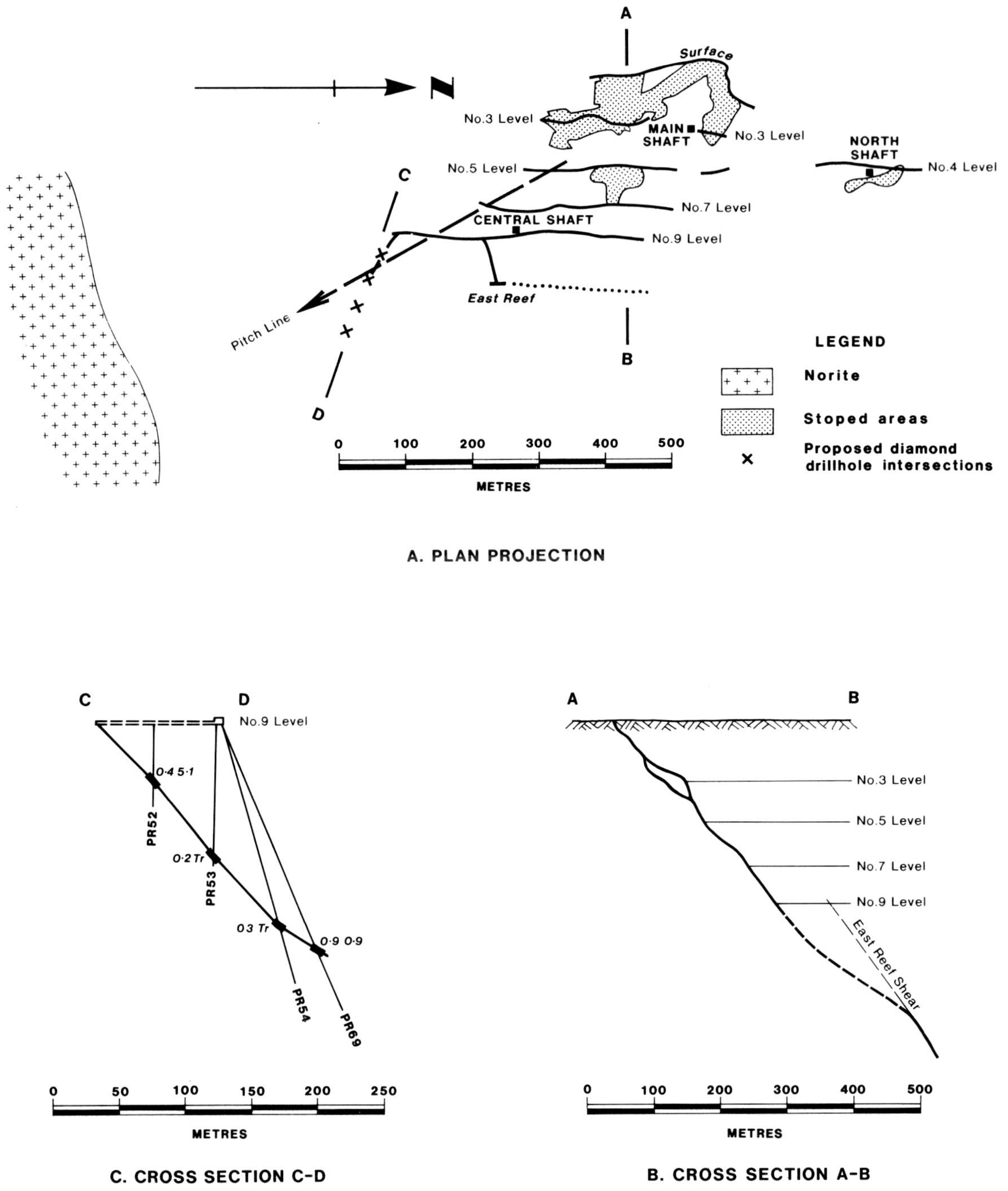

Figure 38

Figure 38 A. Plan projection of old Princess Royal mine showing pitch line of orebody and proposed diamond drilling.
B. Cross section A-B looking north showing known and postulated reef pattern.
C. Cross section C-D looking north showing diamond drilling results.

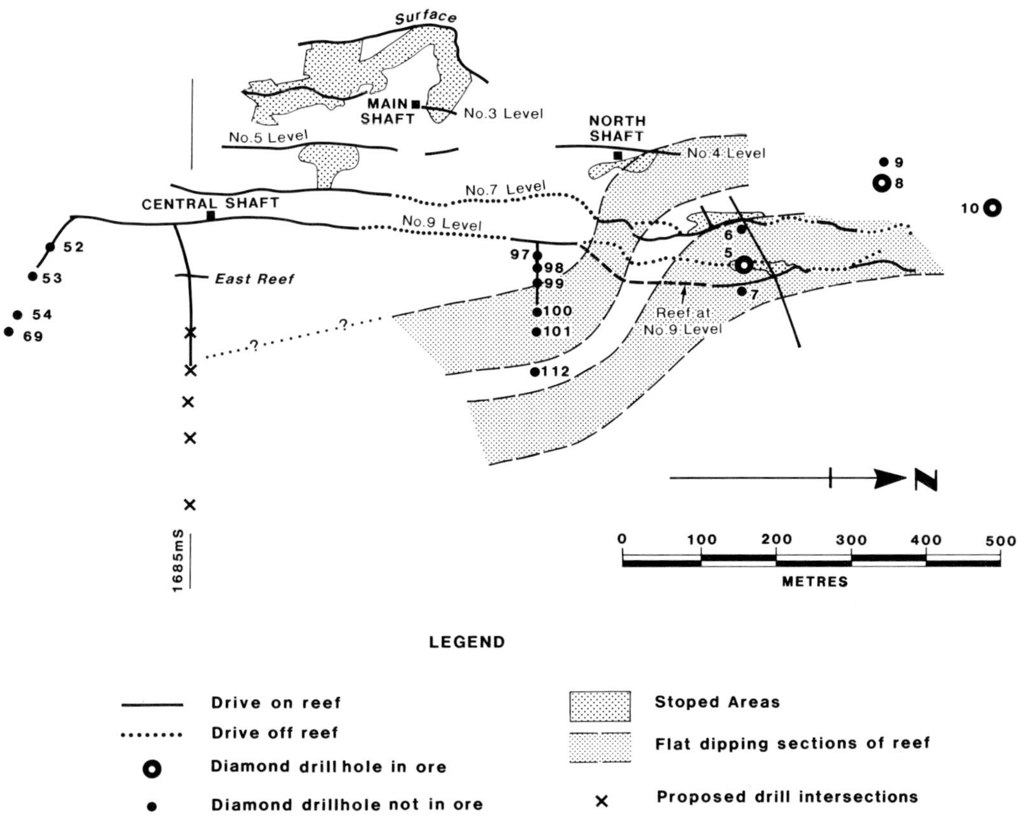

Figure 39 Plan projection of the Princess Royal reef showing proposal for deep diamond drilling test at coordinate 1685mS.

Figure 39

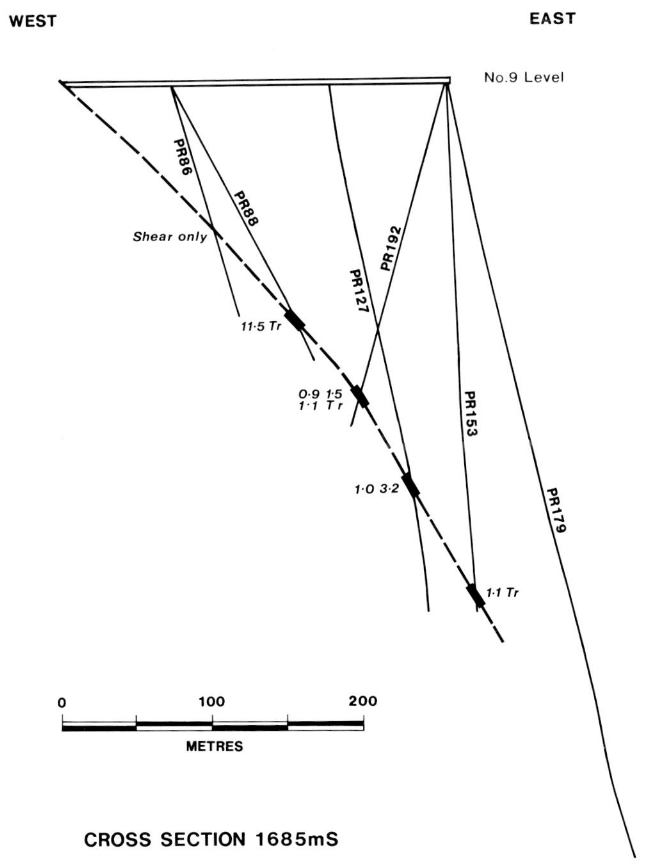

Figure 40

Figure 40 Cross section looking north at coordinate 1685mS showing diamond drilling results.

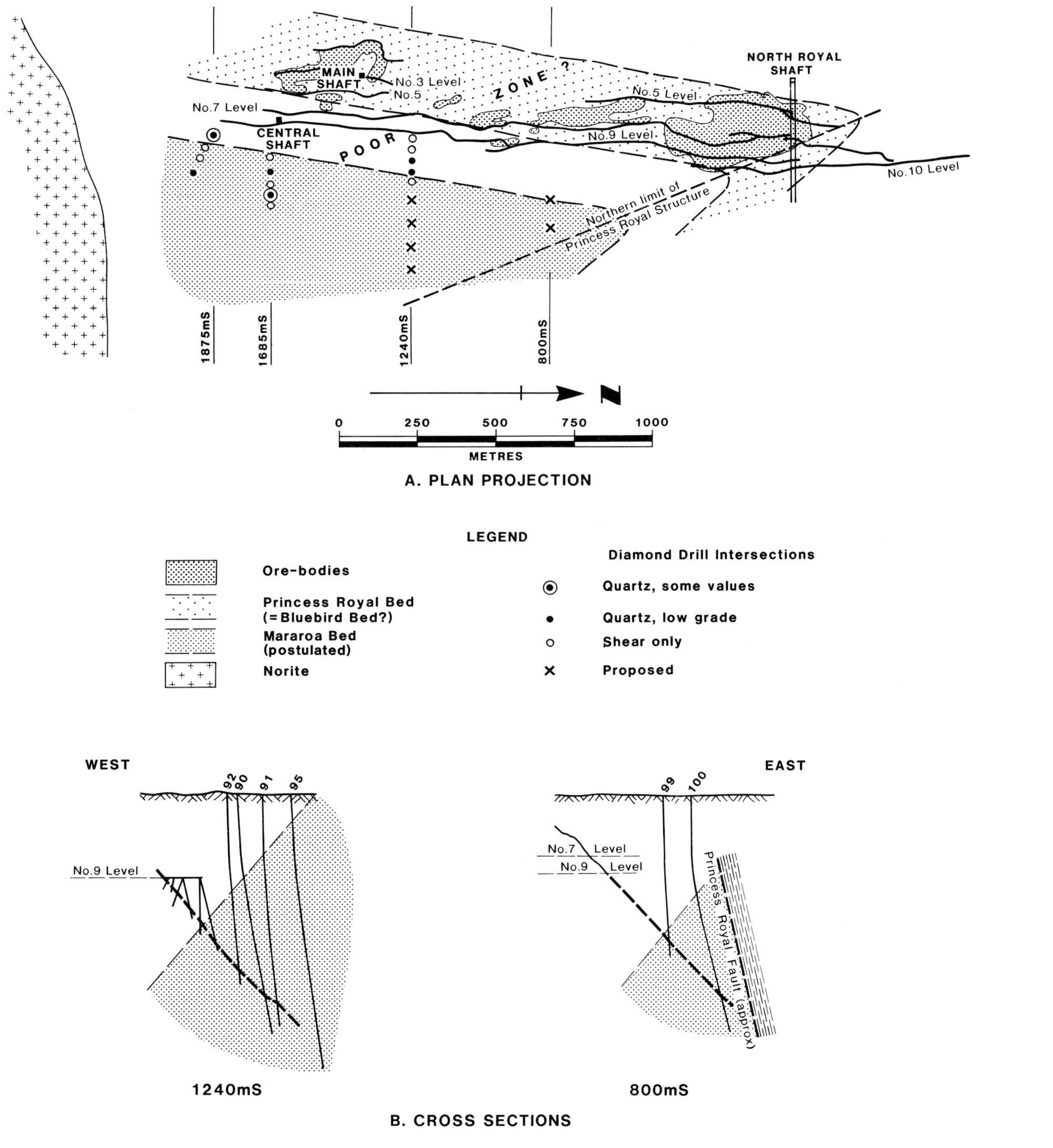

Figure 41 A. Plan projection of the Princess Royal reef showing proposal for diamond drilling in the postulated Mararoa bed — after Report K/1096.
B. Cross sections looking north showing diamond drilling.

Figure 41

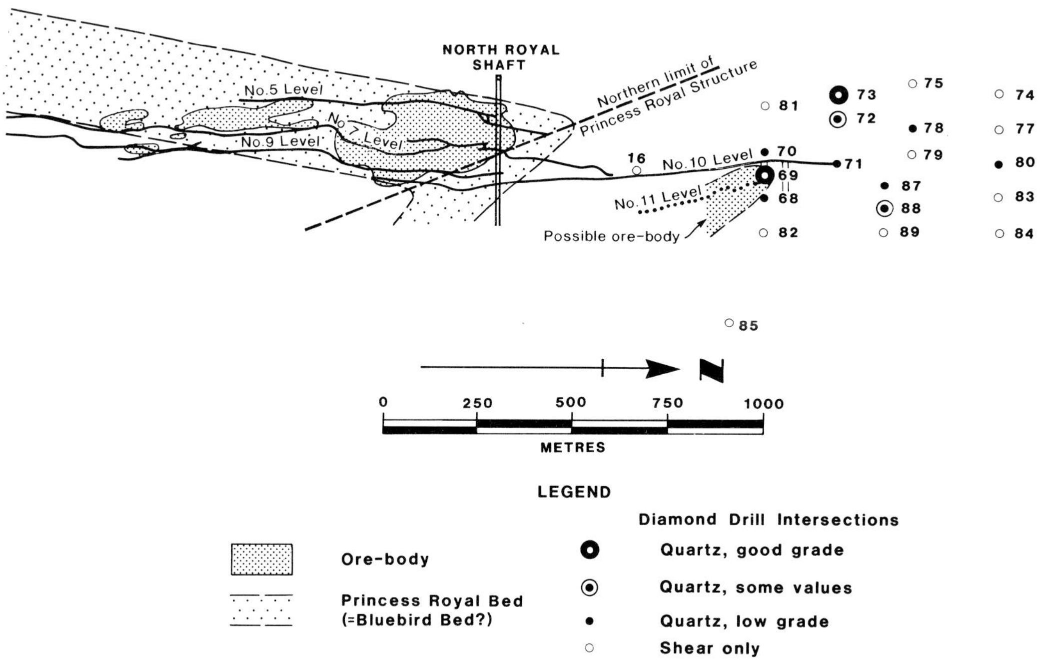

Figure 42

Figure 42 Plan projection of the Princess Royal reef showing diamond drilling results and development to the north of the North Royal shaft — after Report K/1096.

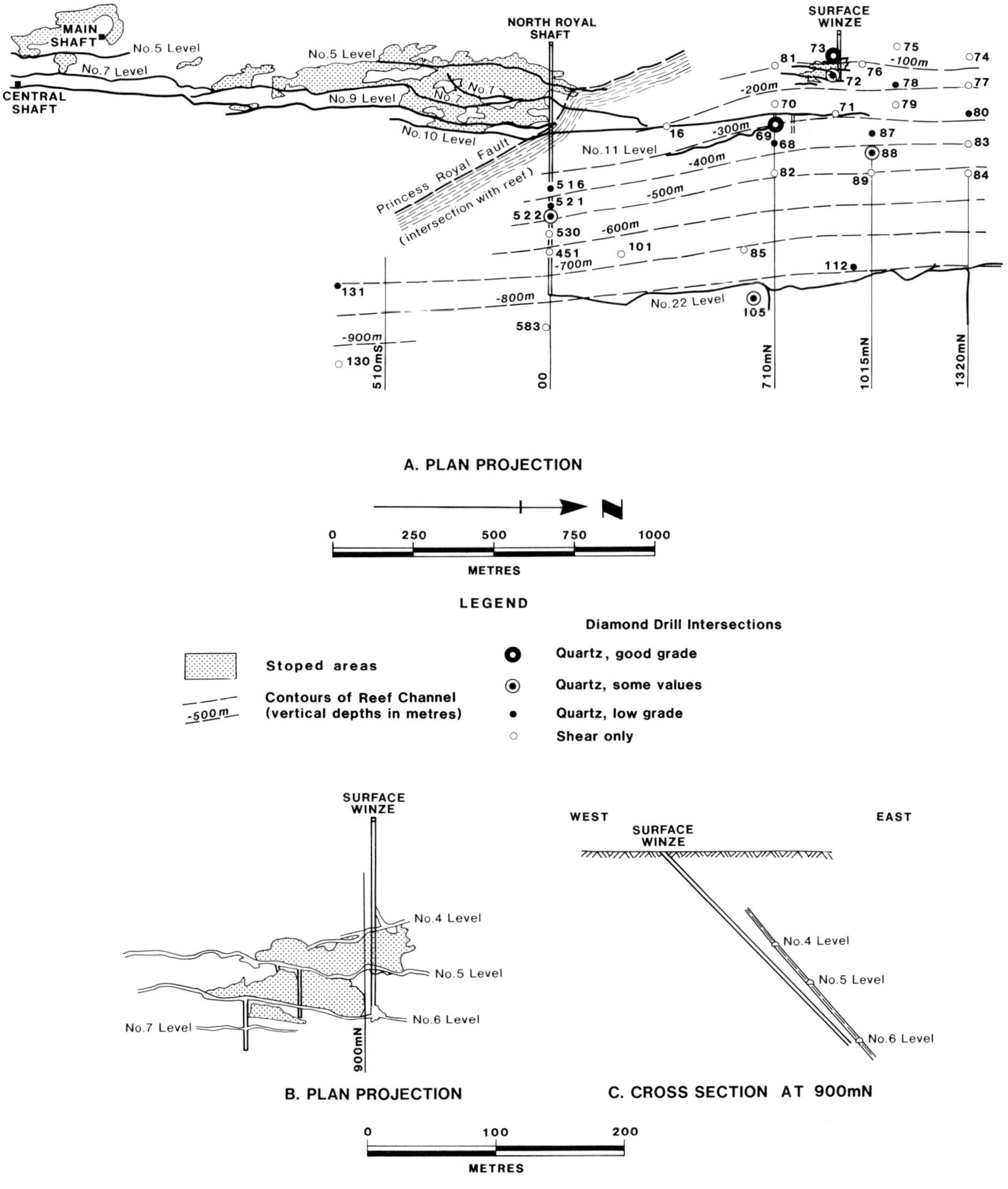

Figure 43 A. Plan projection of the Princess Royal reef showing diamond drilling results and development to the north of the Princess Royal fault.
B. Plan projection of the near-surface workings.
C. Cross section looking north showing reef and Surface Winze.

Figure 43

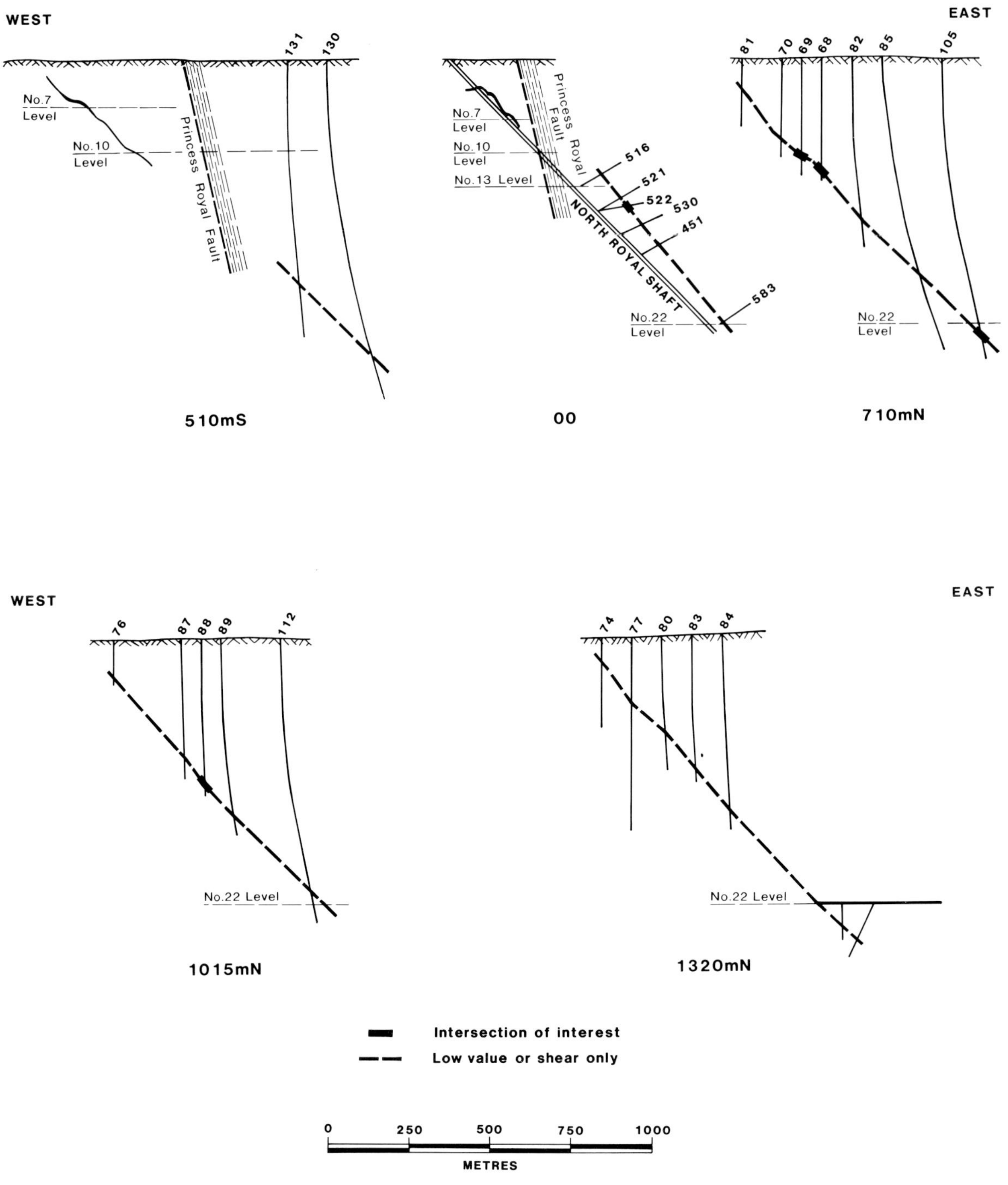

Figure 44

Figure 44 Cross sections looking north relating to Figure 43A.

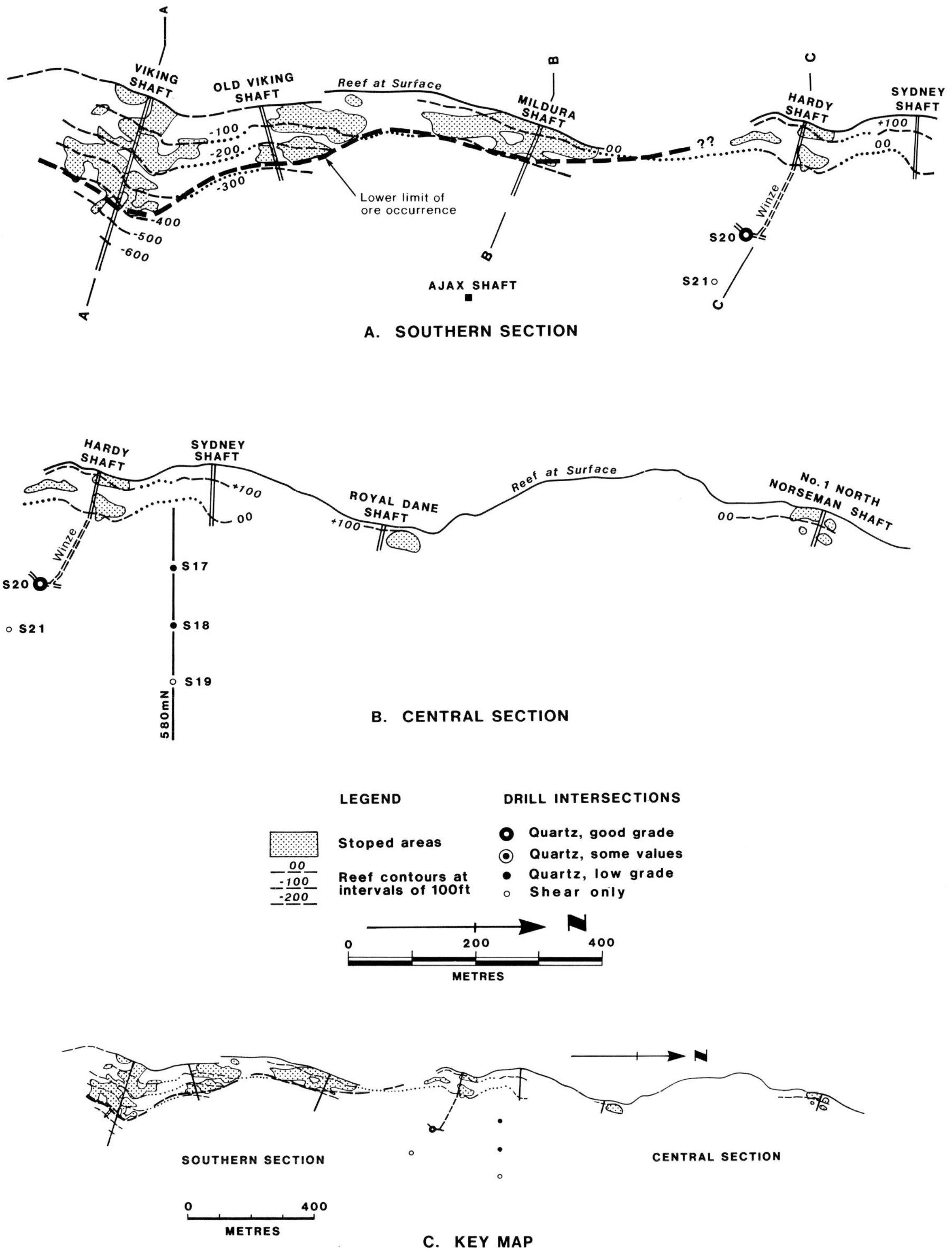

Figure 45 Plan projections showing the outcrop of the Norseman reef and the workings on it. The reef contours are at 100 ft vertical intervals; the datum is the collar level at the Phoenix shaft.

Figure 45

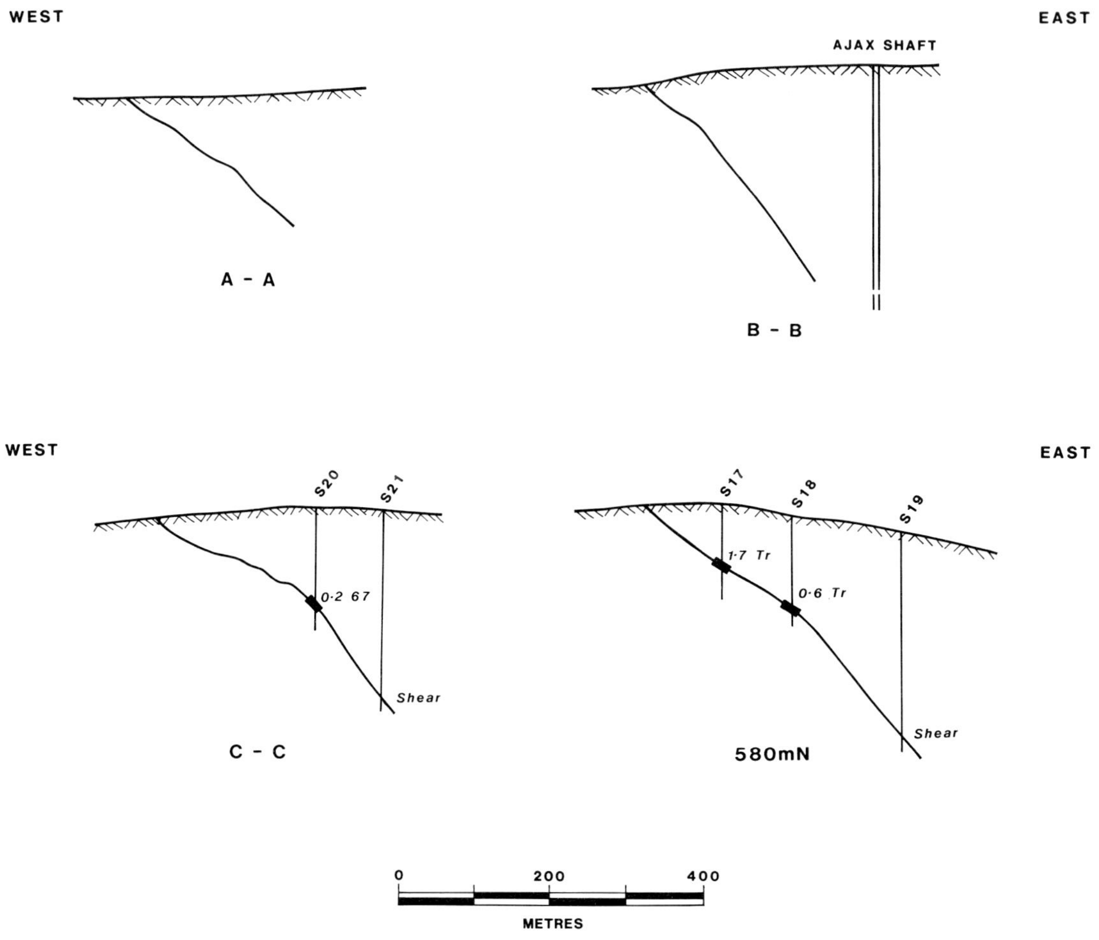

Figure 46

Figure 46 Cross sections relating to Figure 45, looking north.
A-A Viking, B-B Mildura, C-C Hardy.

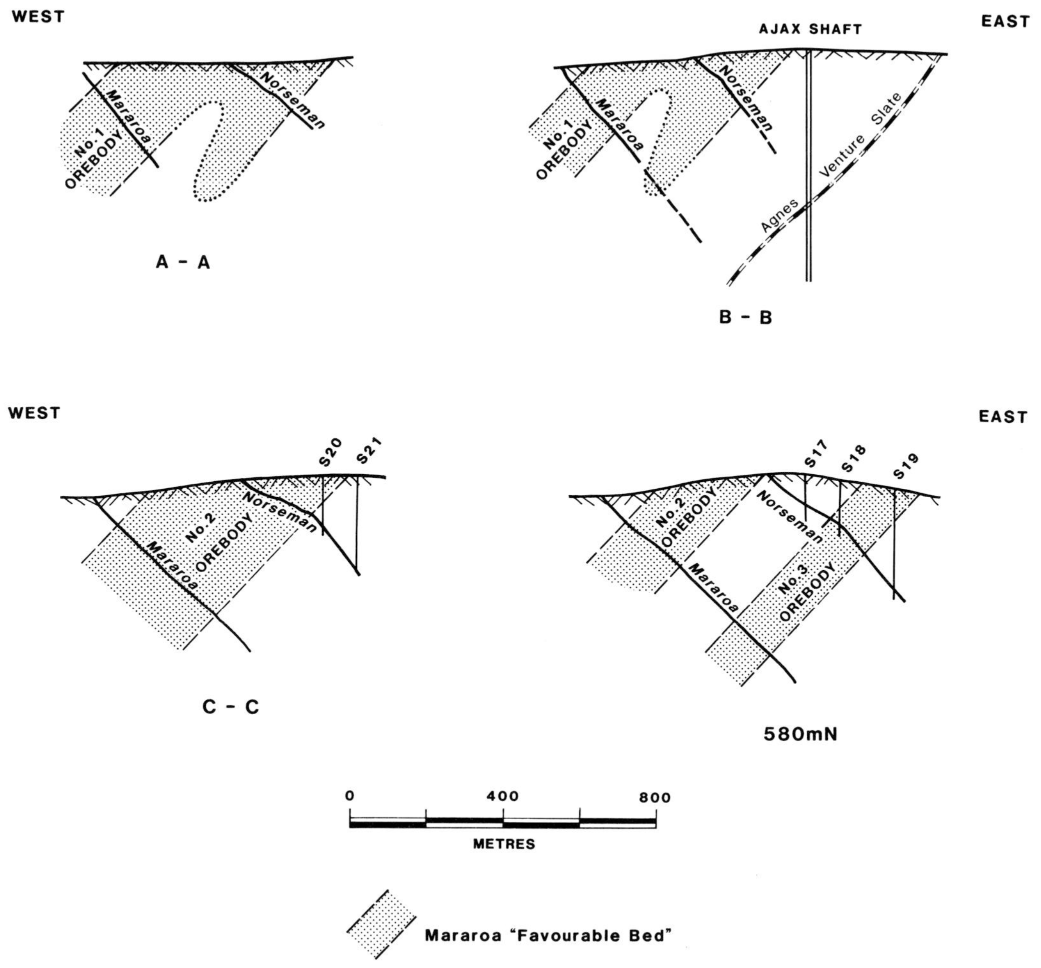

Figure 47 The cross sections of Figure 46 at a reduced scale to show the Mararoa reef and the presumed trend of the Mararoa bed.

Figure 47

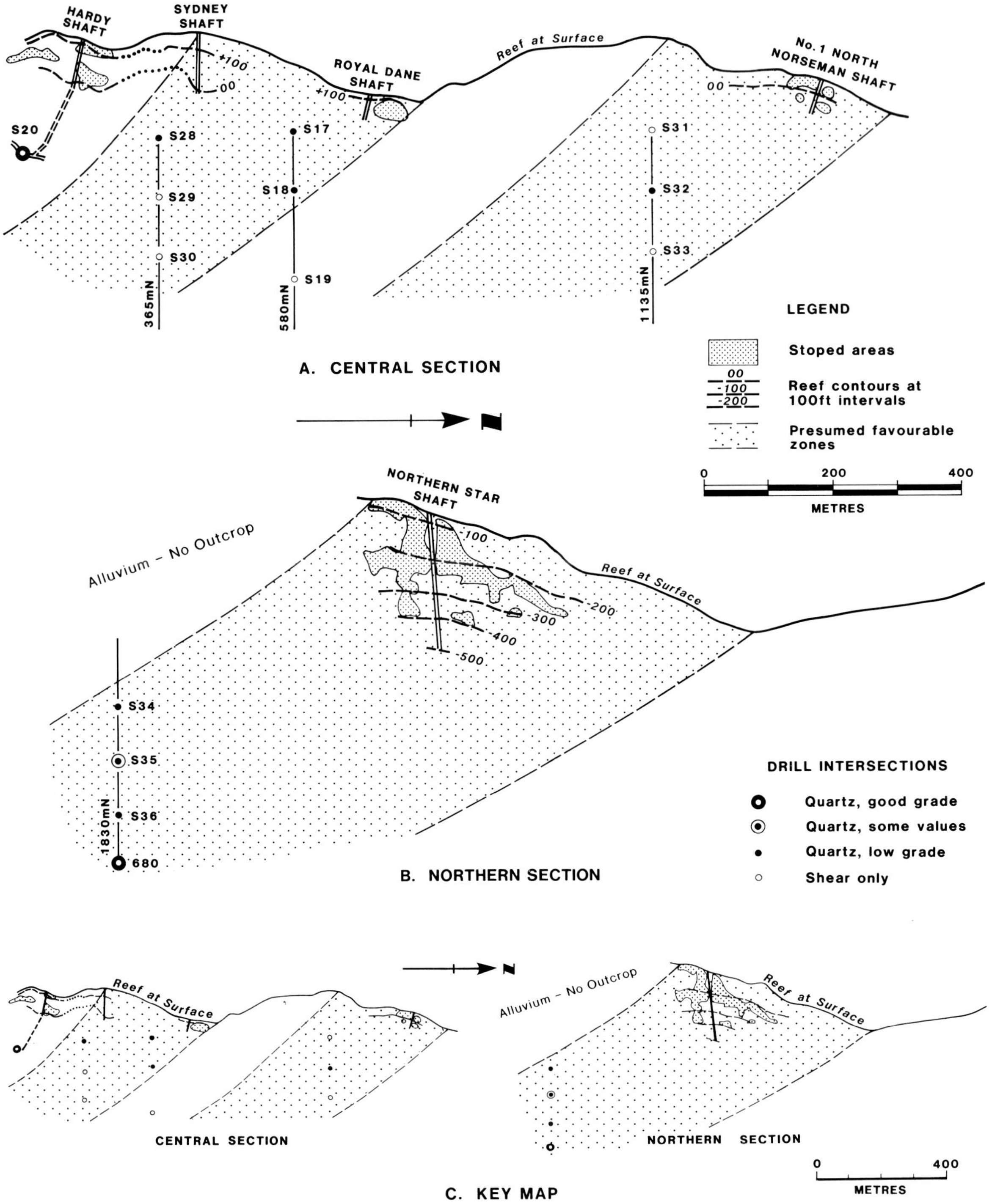

Figure 48

Figure 48 Plan projection showing the outcrops of the Norseman and Northern Star reefs and the workings on them. (Figure 45B has been repeated as Figure 48A). The reef contours are at 100 ft vertical intervals.

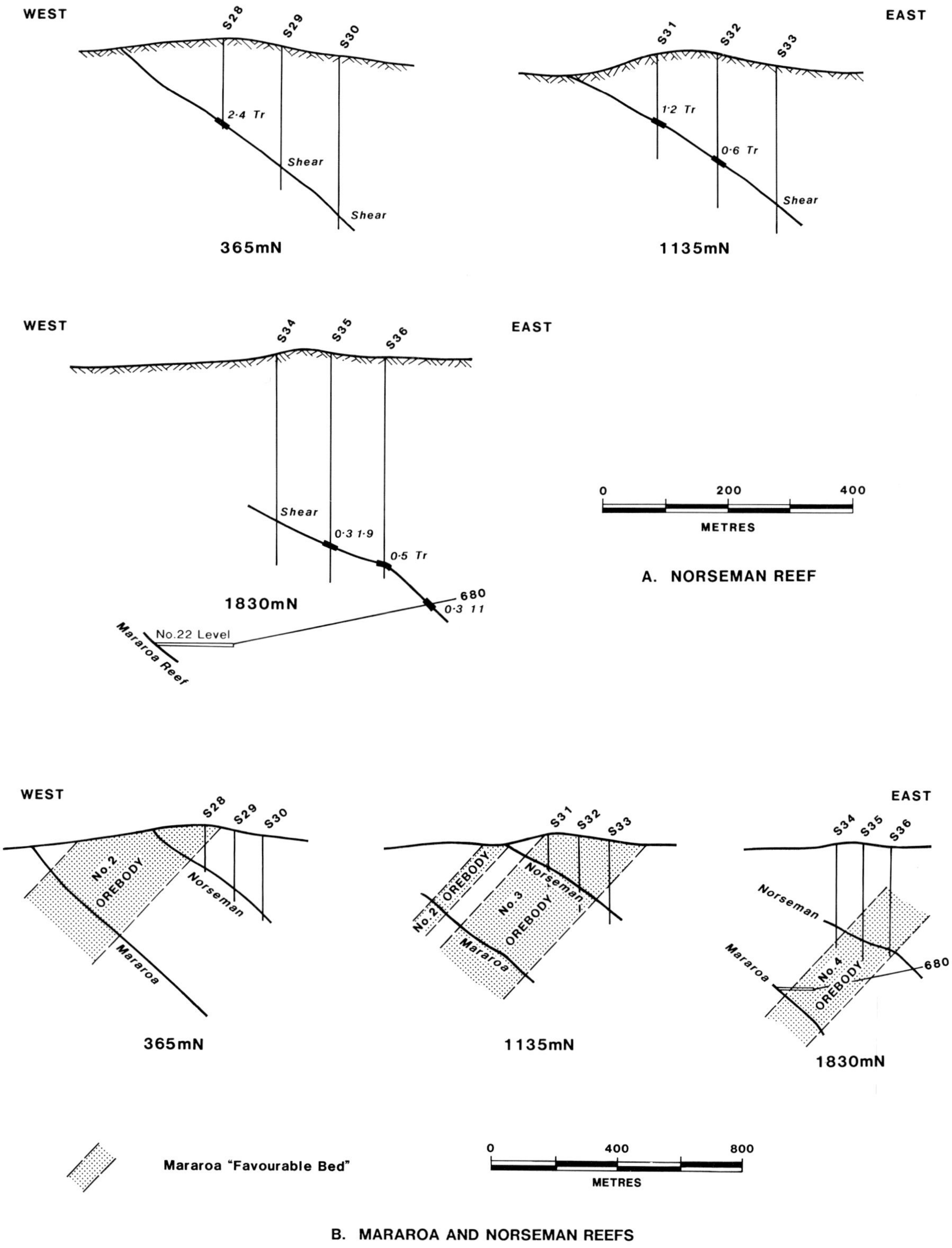

Figure 49

Figure 49 Cross sections relating to Figure 48, looking north. The lower group is at a reduced scale to show the Mararoa reef and the presumed trend of the Mararoa bed.

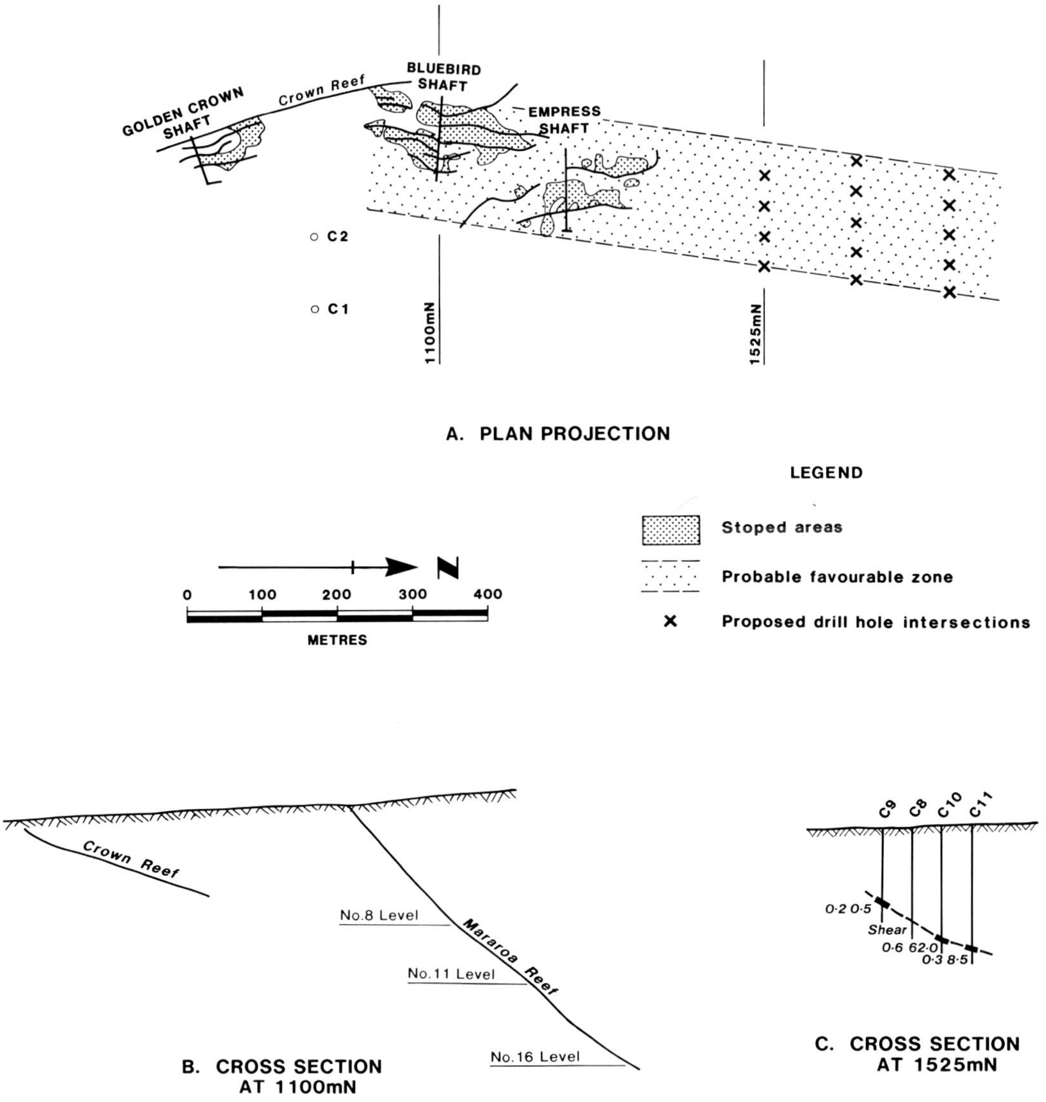

Figure 50

Figure 50 A. Plan projection showing the workings on the Crown reef, the estimated northerly trend of the favourable zone and proposed diamond drill holes.
B. and C. Cross sections looking north.

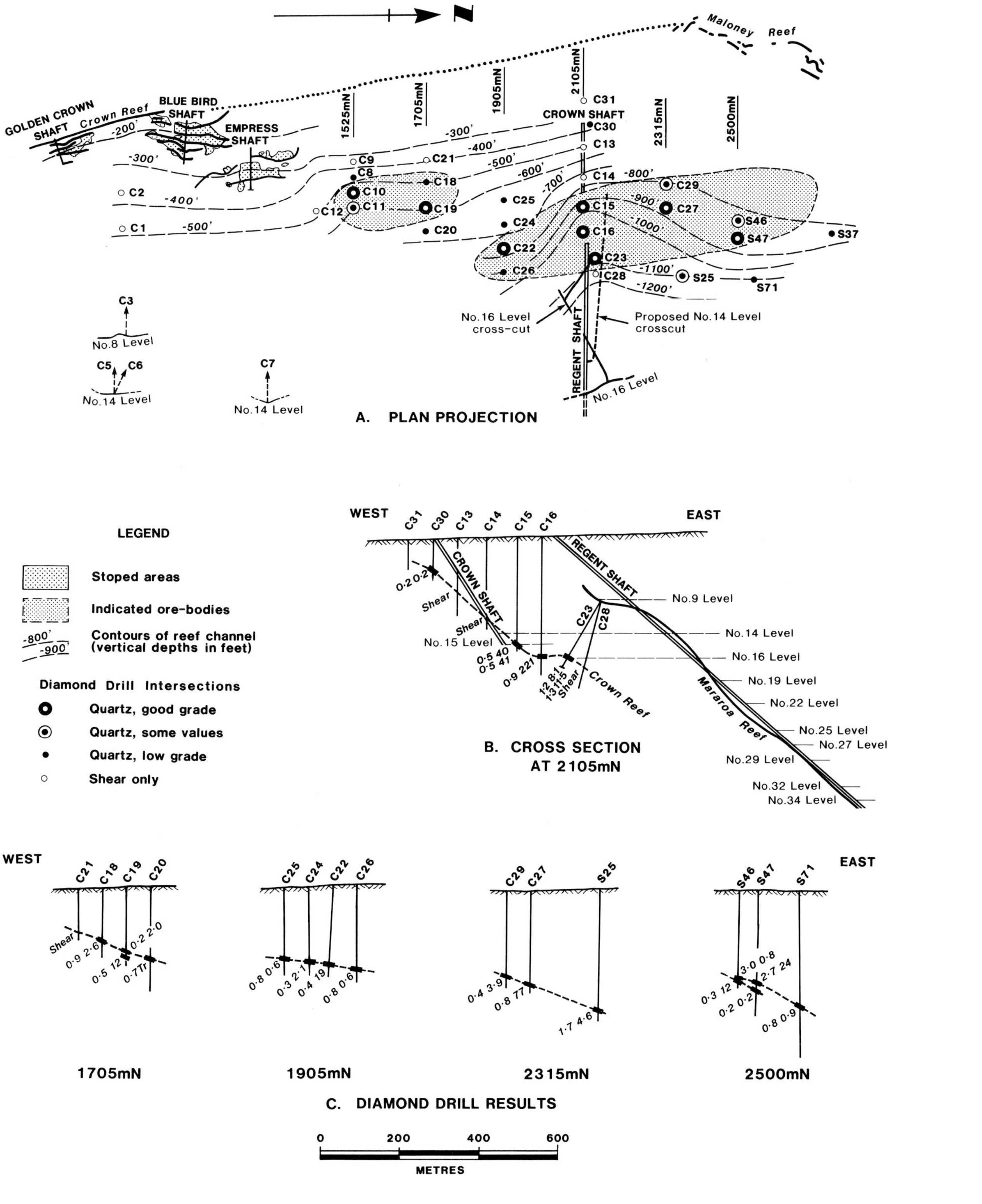

Figure 51 A. Plan projection of the Crown reef showing diamond drilling results, new ore areas and the presumed connection between the Crown and Maloney reefs at the surface. The reef contours are at 100 ft vertical intervals; datum Phoenix shaft collar. Holes marked C1 to C7 are unsuccessful ones drilled by Central Norseman in the late 1930's.

B. and C. Cross sections looking north.

Figure 51

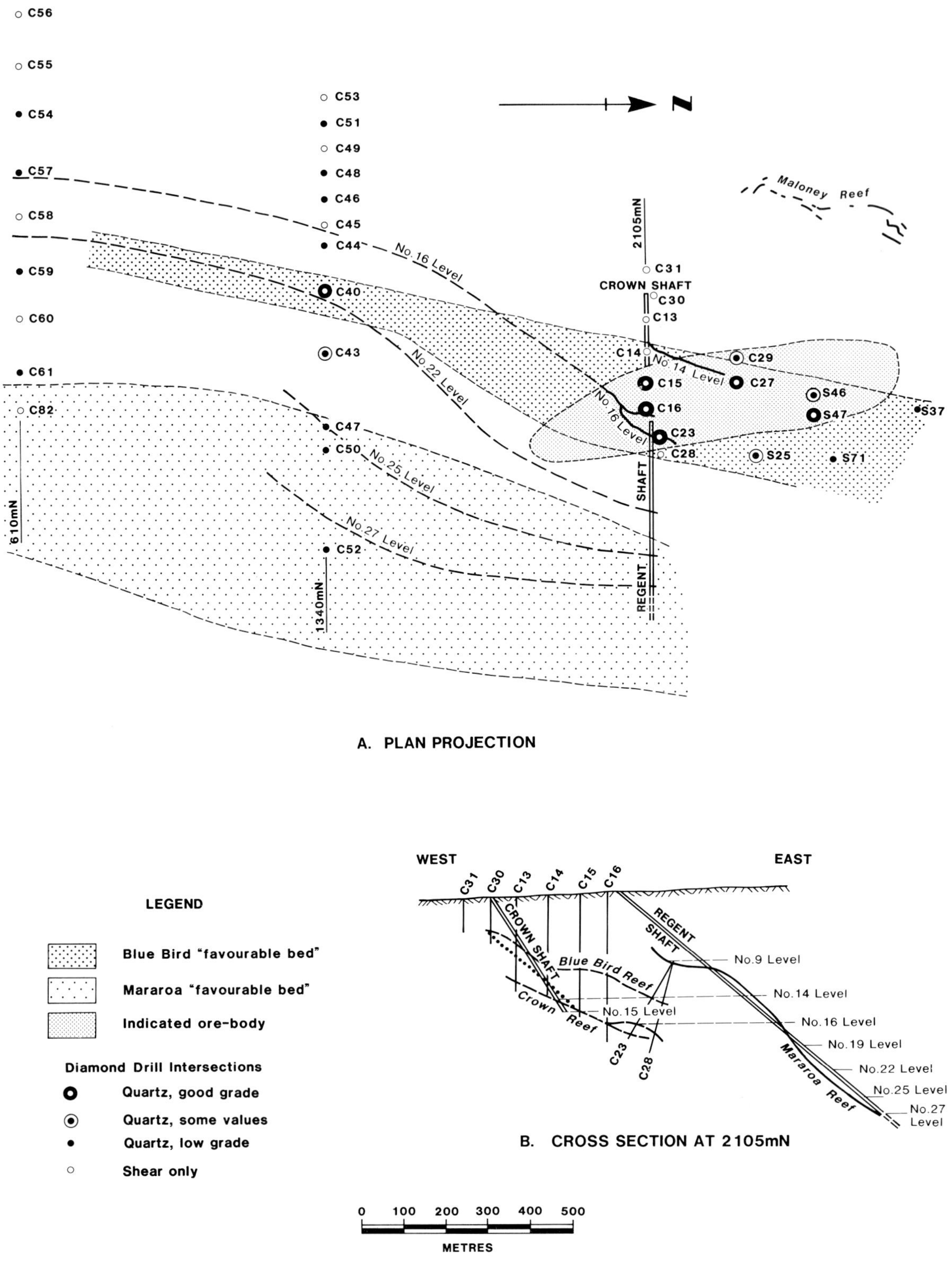

Figure 52

Figure 52 A. Plan projection of the Crown reef showing the south-westerly trend of No. 16 level to the south of the Regent shaft and the results of the new programme of deeper diamond drilling.

B. Cross section, looking north, showing the mis-tie (the dotted line) that led to erroneous tie between the Maloney reef and the original Crown reef in Figure 51A.

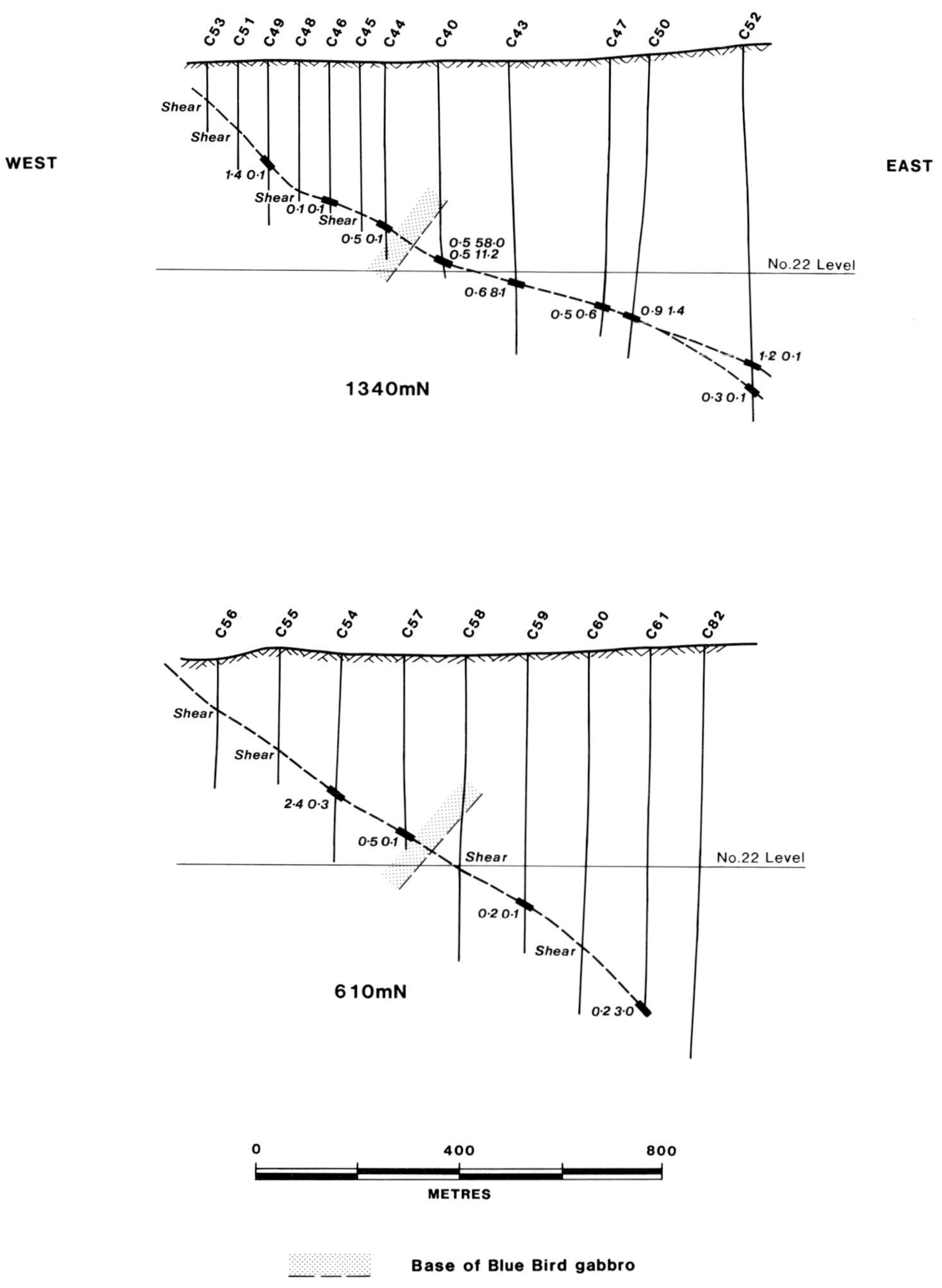

Figure 53 Cross sections of the Crown reef looking north showing diamond drilling results — see Figure 52A.

Figure 53

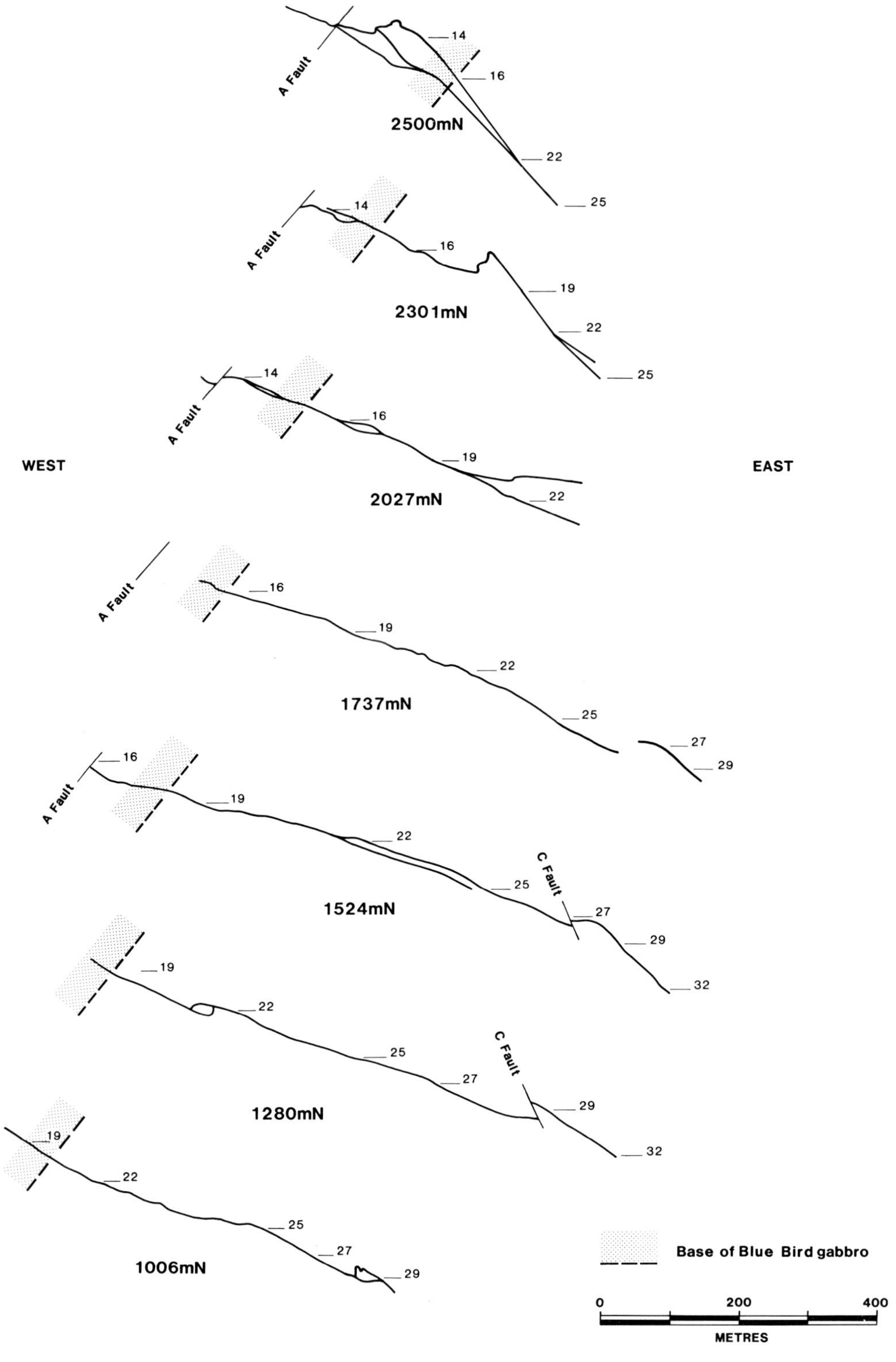

Figure 54

Figure 54 Cross sections looking north showing the Crown reef. For locations, see Plate 13A.

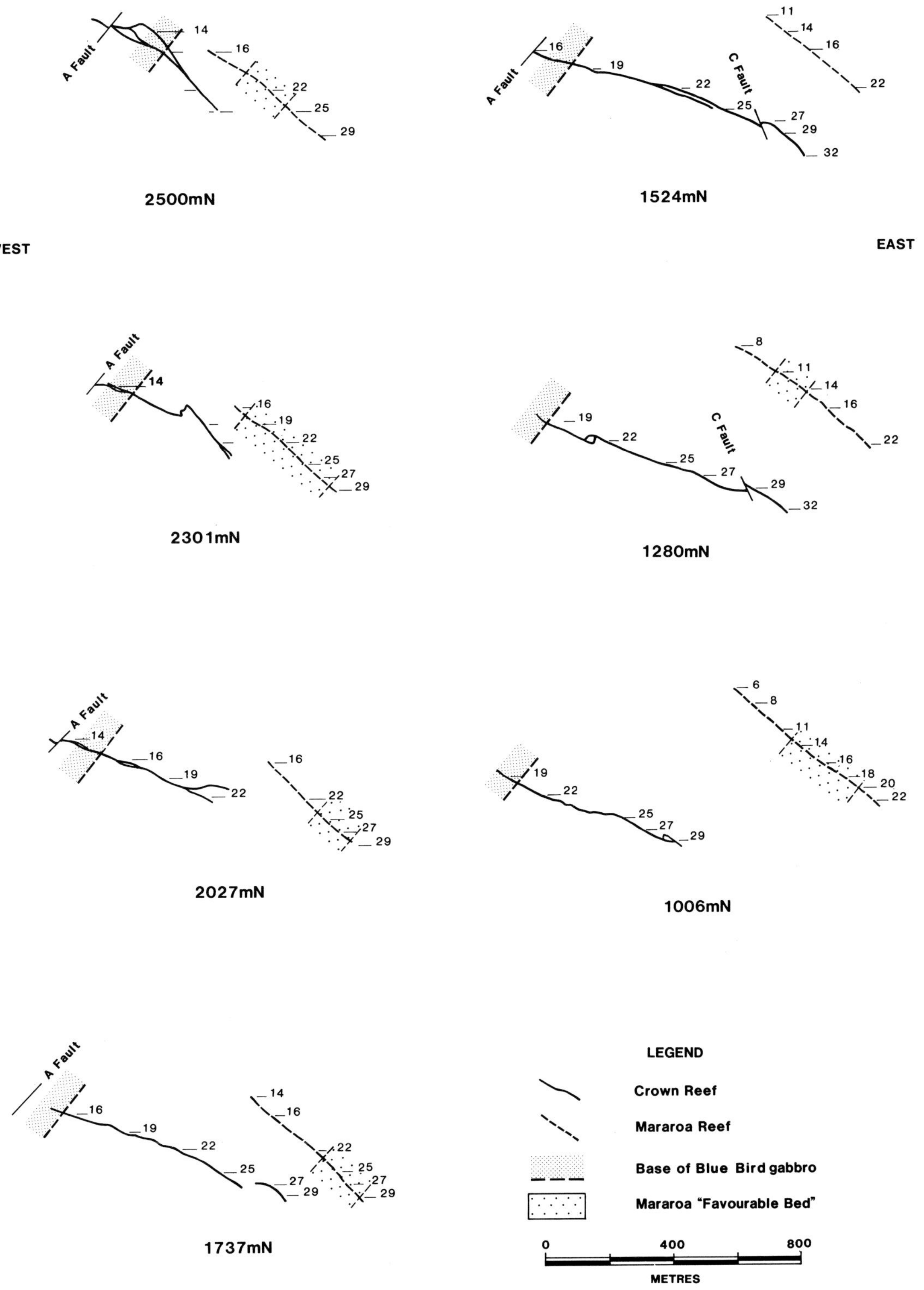

Figure 55 The cross sections of Figure 54 at a reduced scale to show the relationship of the Crown reef to the Mararoa reef and the Mararoa bed.

Figure 55

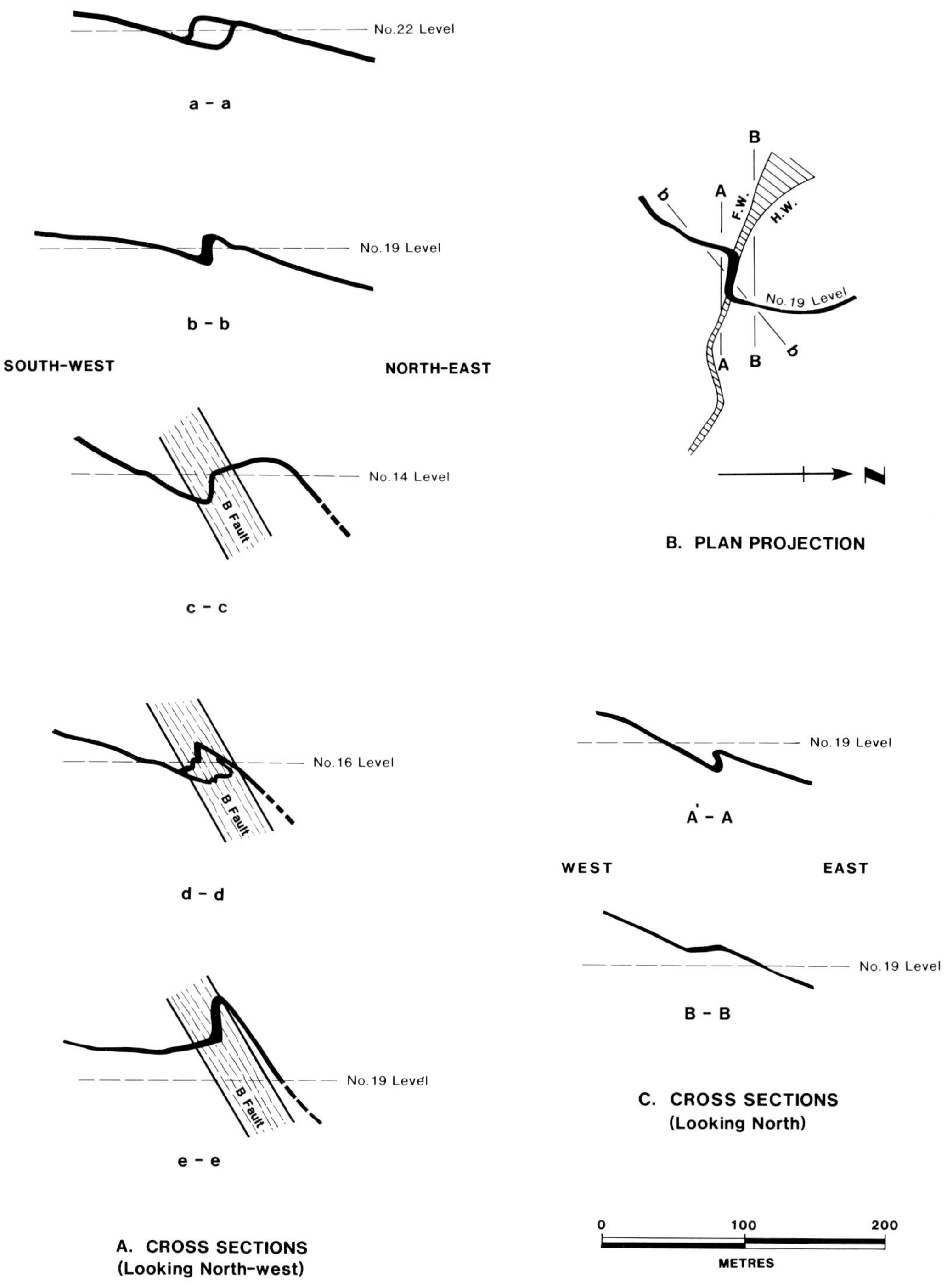

Figure 56

Figure 56 A. Cross sections of the Crown reef showing patterns of behaviour within and around the verticals. For locations, see Plate 13A.
B. Plan projection showing the course of the Crown reef on No. 19 level, with hatchured areas showing the limits of stoping on the vertical above and below the level.
C. Cross sections looking north — locations shown in Figure 56B. Cross section b-b is given in Figure 56A.

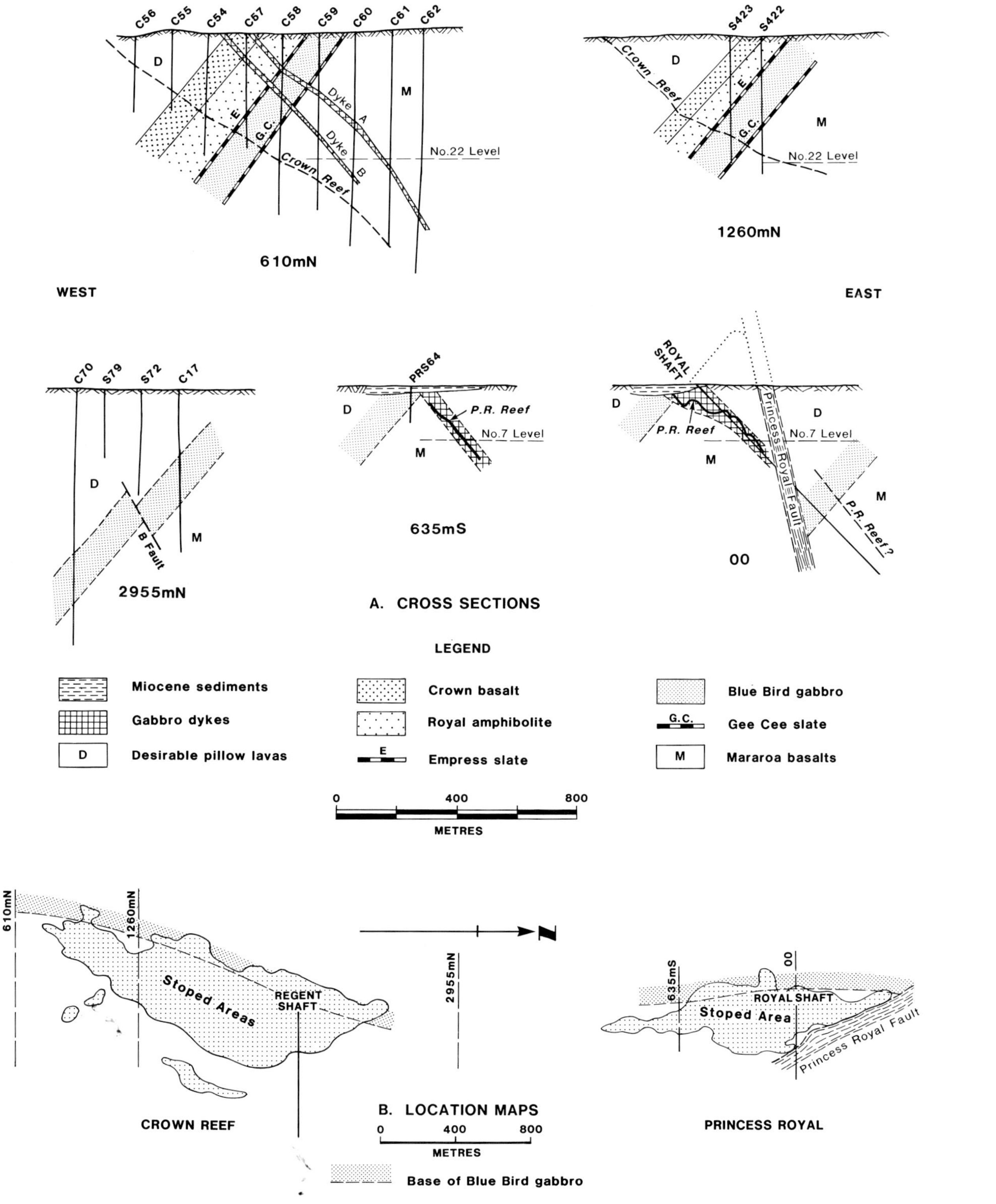

Figure 57 A. Cross sections looking north showing the Blue Bird sequence and, at Princess Royal, an east-dipping dyke, the host of the reef.
B. Plan projections giving locations of cross sections.

Figure 57

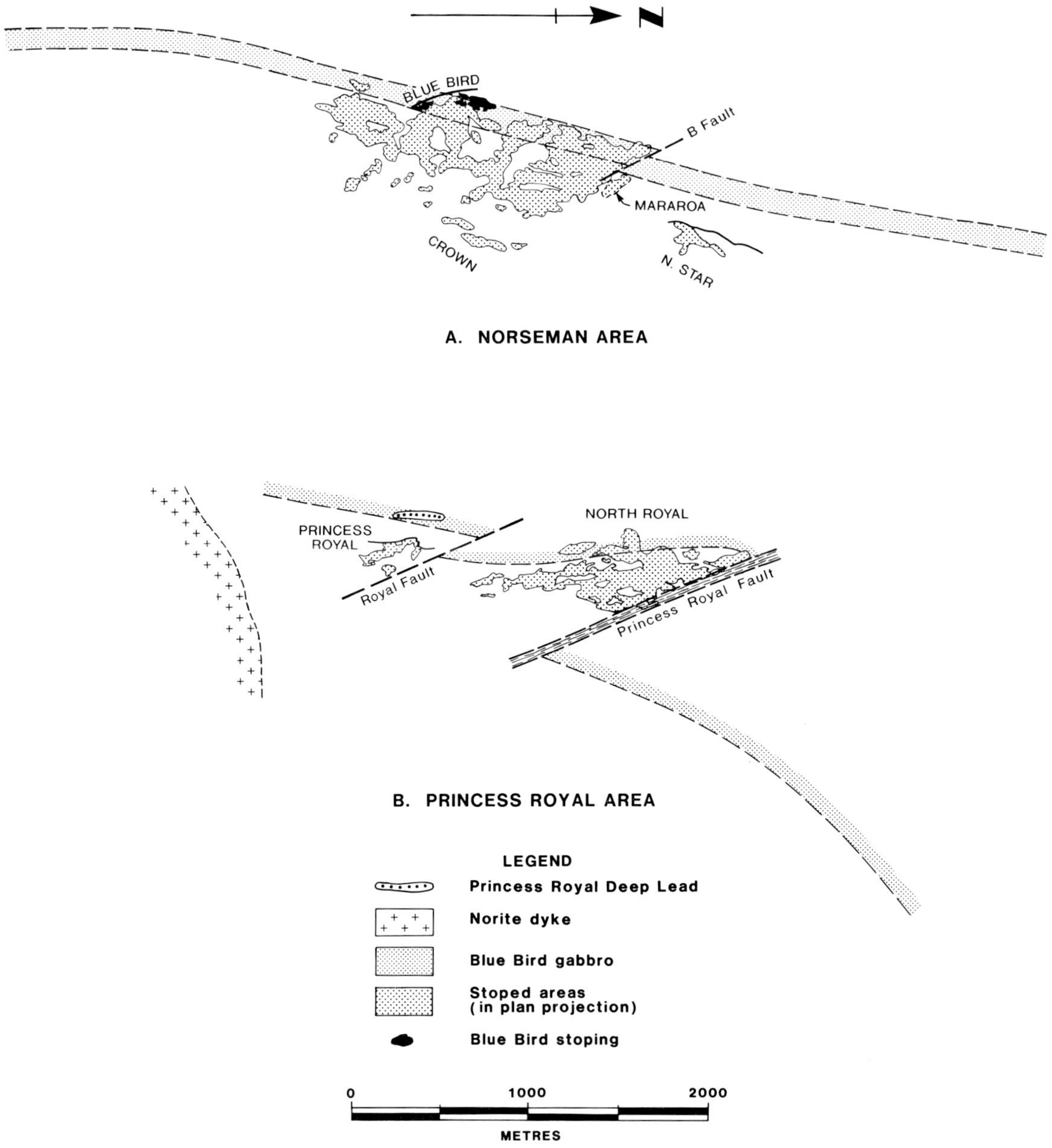

Figure 58

Figure 58 Plan projections showing the relationship between stoped areas and the interpreted surface position of the Blue Bird gabbro.
In Figure 58A, the position of the Crown reef stoping is schematic, as is explained in the text.
In Figure 58B, only the foot-wall of the Blue Bird gabbro is known.

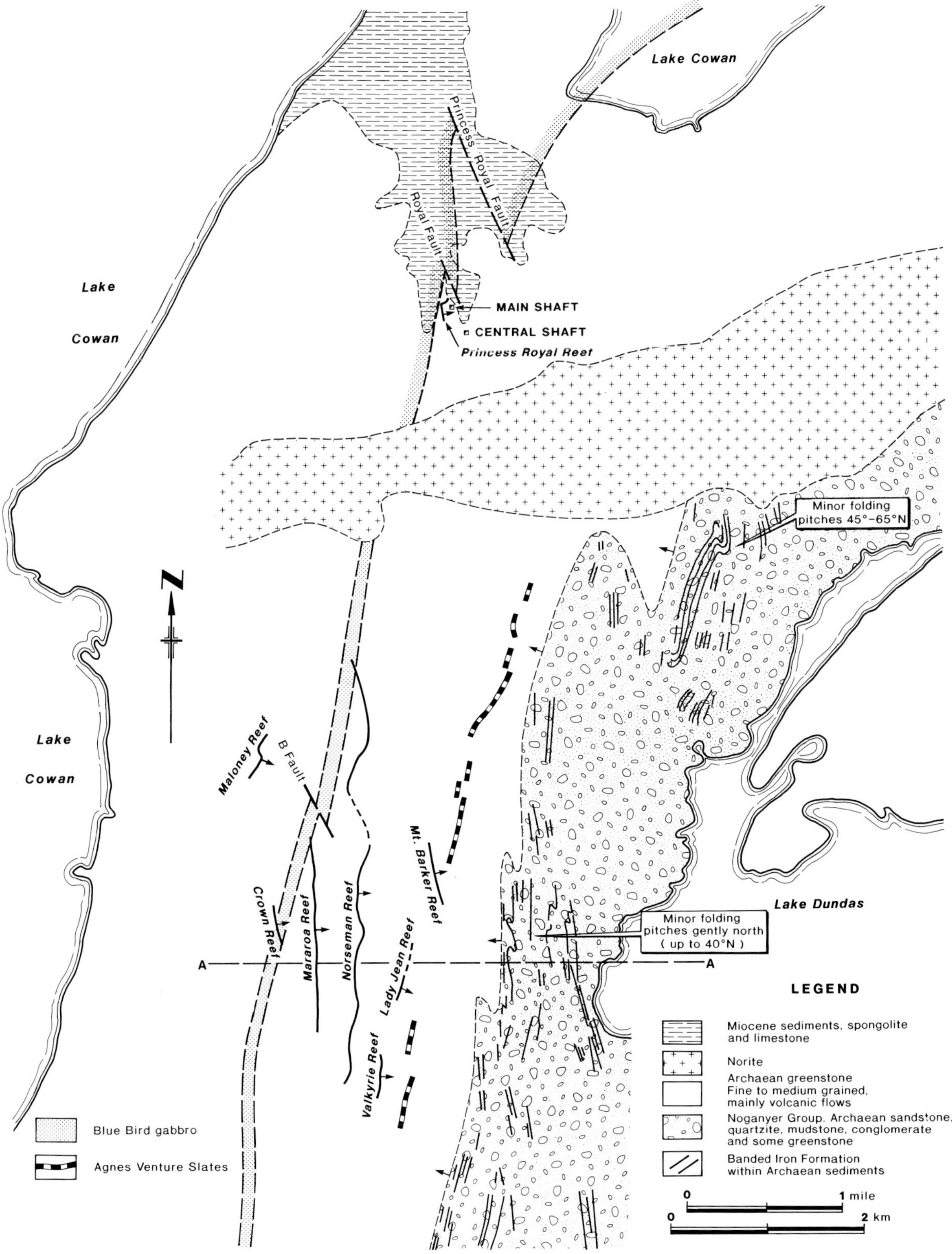

Figure 59

Figure 59 Figure 1, repeated with the addition of the interpreted surface position of the Blue Bird gabbro and the main outcrops of the Agnes Venture slates.

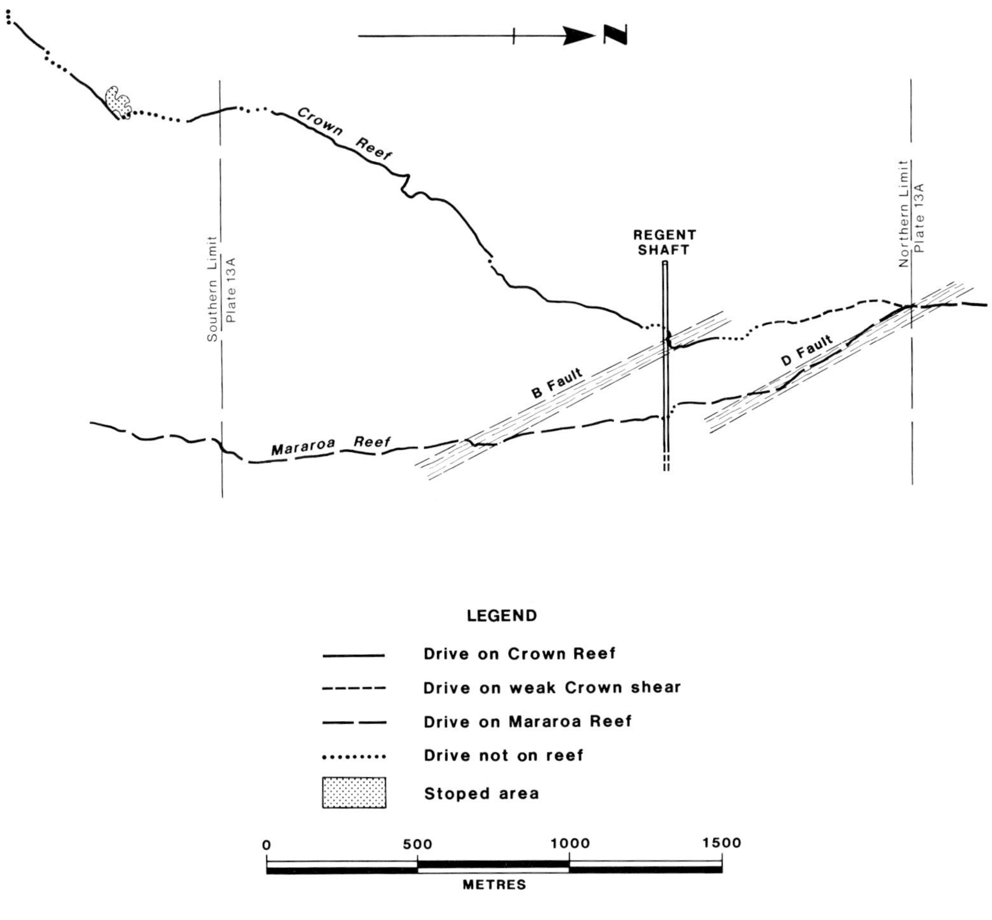

Figure 60

Figure 60 Plan of No. 22 level showing the course of the Crown reef in relation to that of the Mararoa reef.

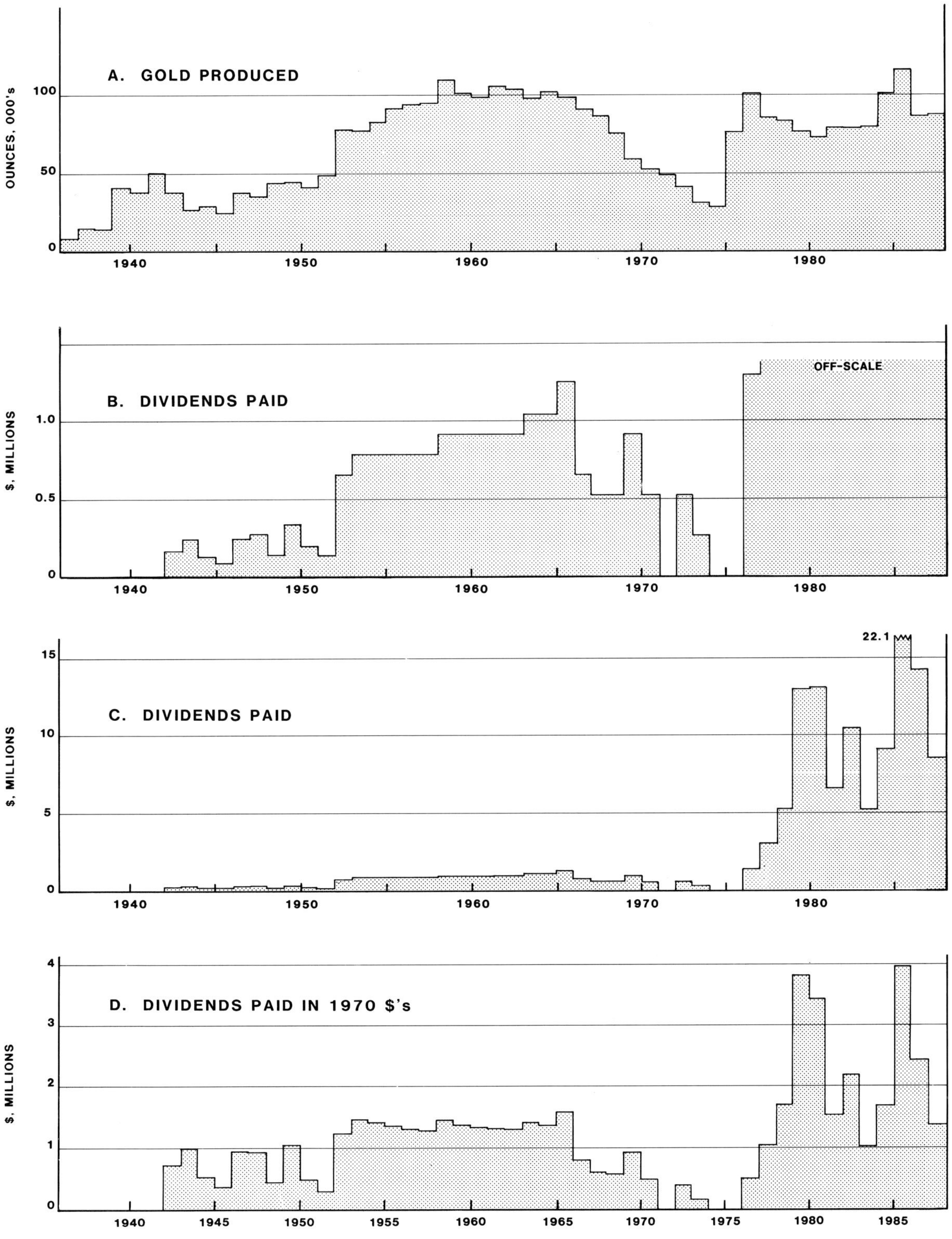

Figure 61

Figure 61 Gold produced and dividends paid 1937-1988.

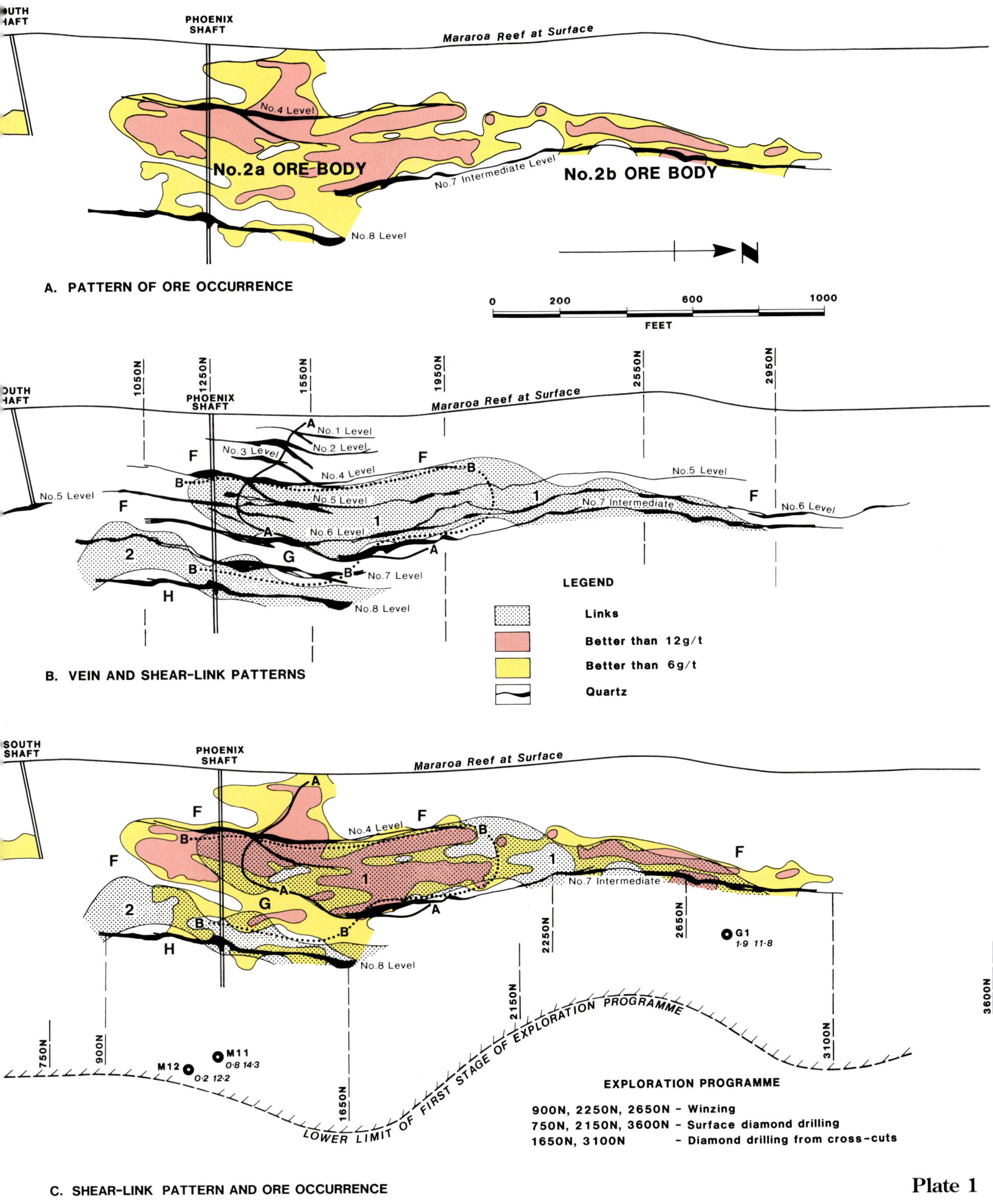

Plate 1

Plate 1 Plan projections of the Mararoa reef showing reef data and ore outlines — based on Plan No. 2 of Conolly's report 55T/1.

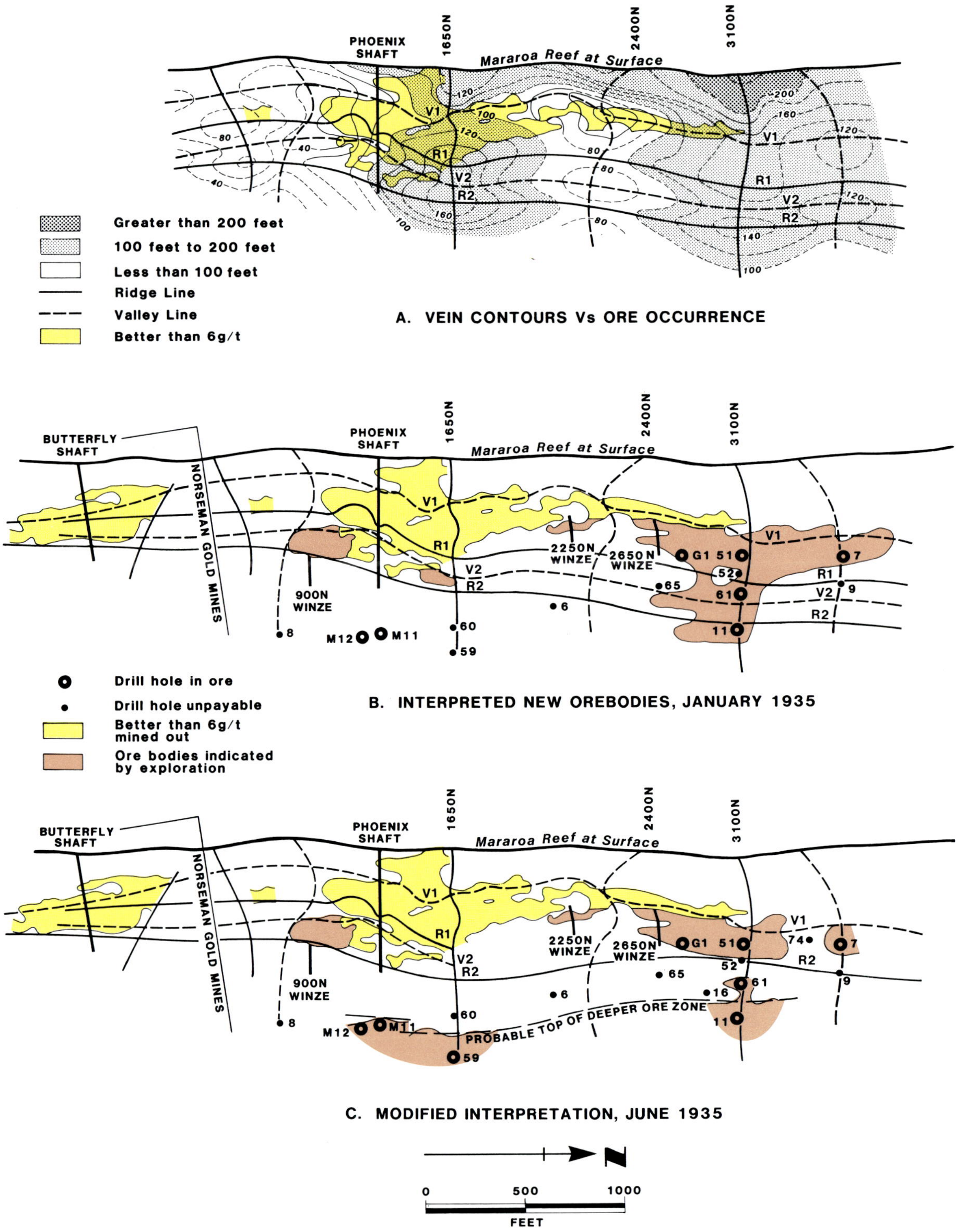

Plate 2

Plate 2 Plan projections of the Mararoa reef.

A. Ore occurrence in relation to the vein contouring versus an inclined plane.

B. Conolly's evaluation of ore potential based on Plate 2A.

C. Conolly's revised interpretation and the deeper ore zone concept.

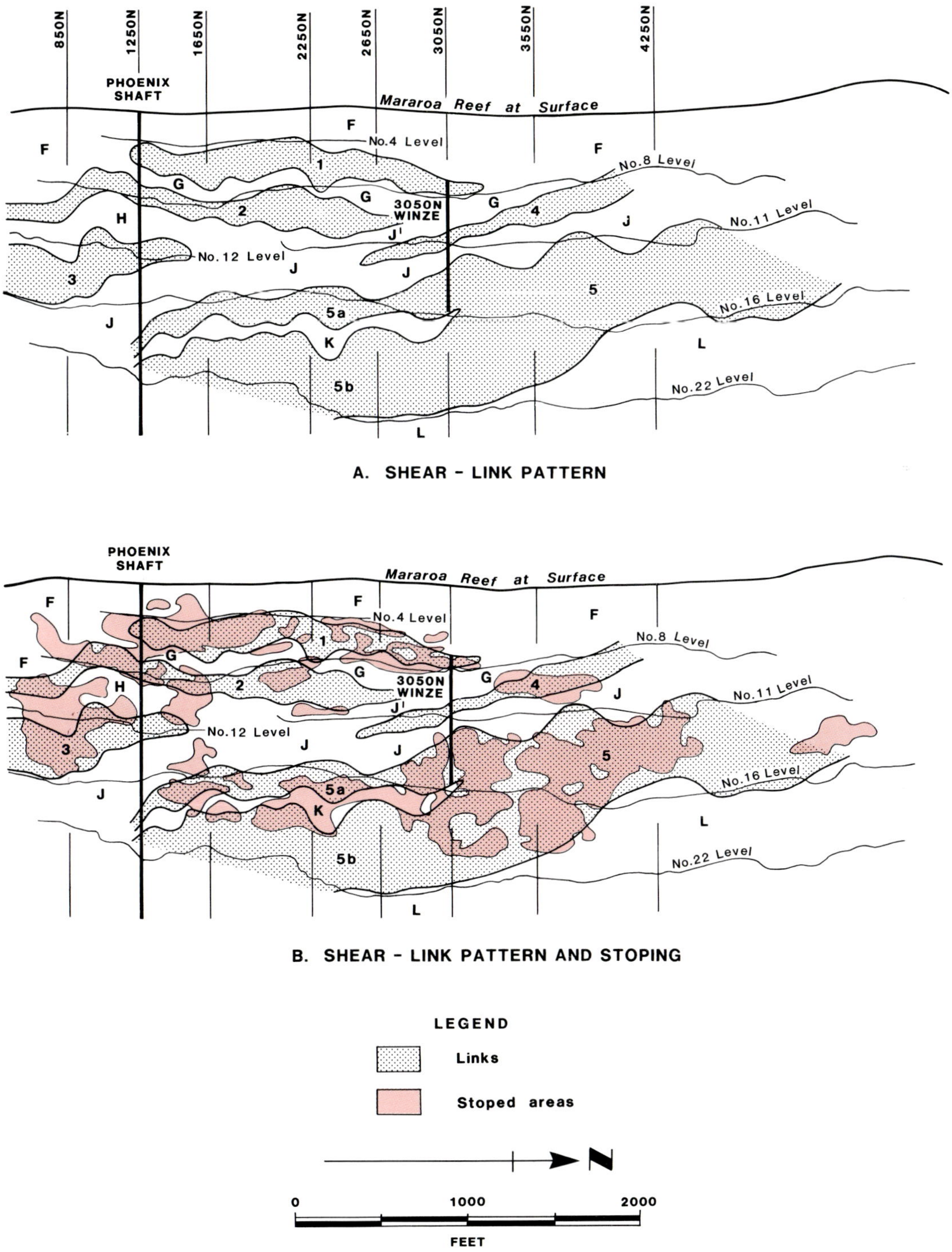

Plate 3 Plan projections of the Mararoa reef.
A. Shear-link pattern.
B. Mined areas superimposed on the shear-link pattern.

Plate 3

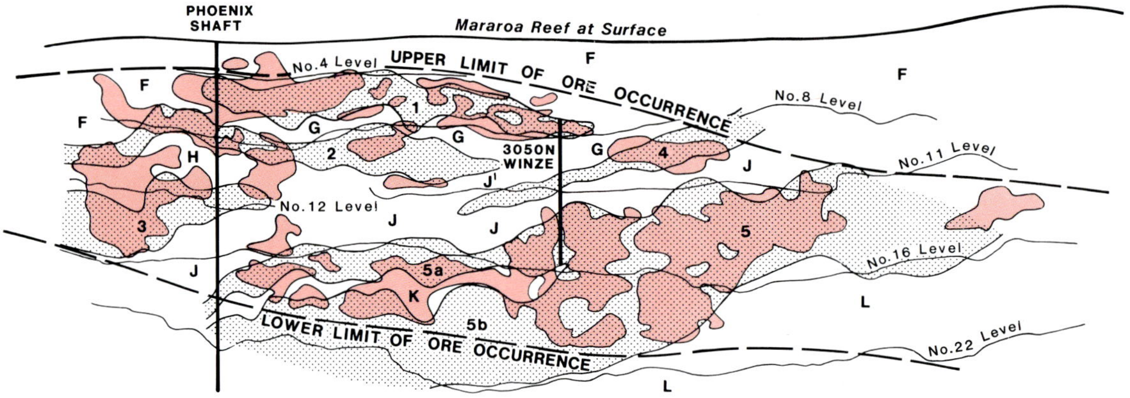

A. UPPER AND LOWER LIMIT OF ORE OCCURRENCE

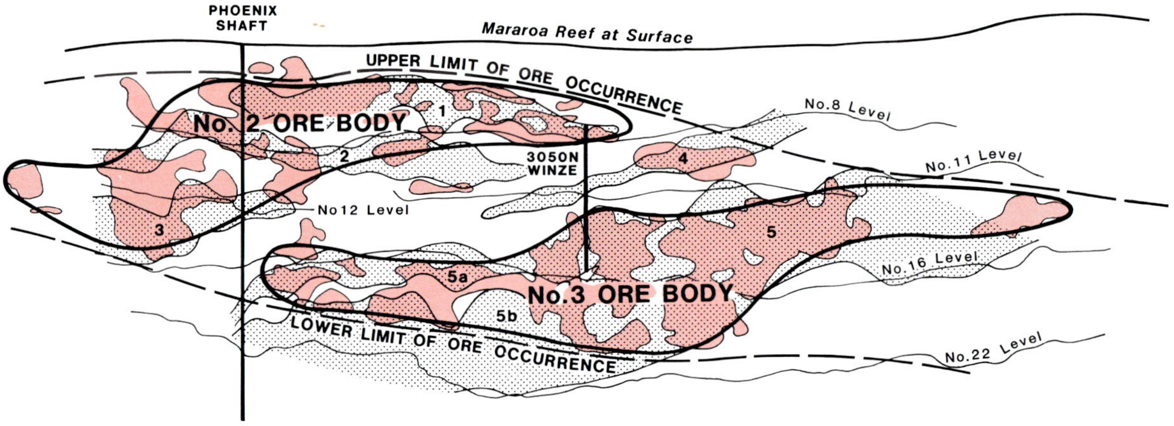

B. ORE BODIES AND LINK PATTERN

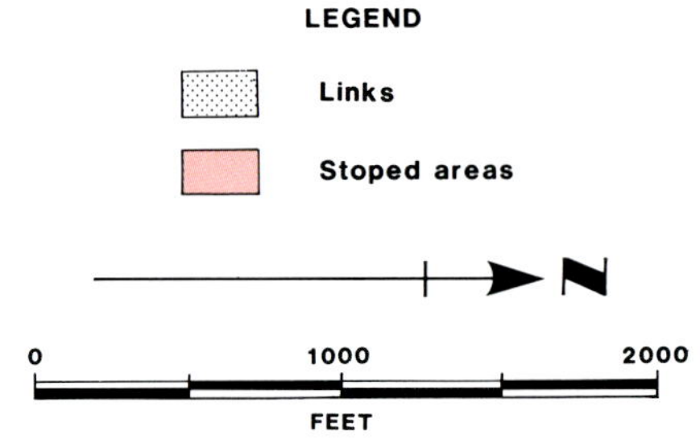

Plate 4

Plate 4 Plan projections of the Mararoa reef.
A. The Limits of ore occurrence.
B. Orebody outlines.

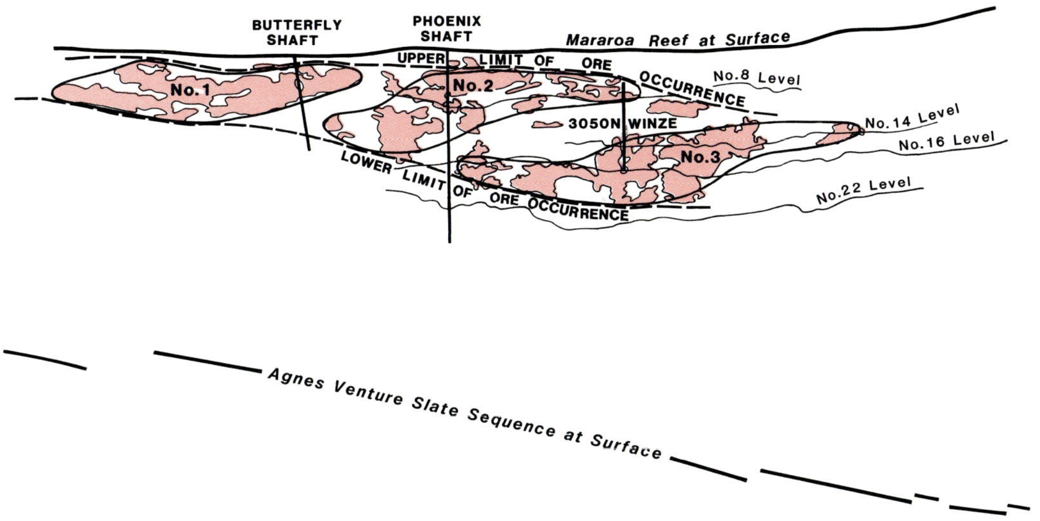

A. DEVELOPMENT AS AT JUNE 1946

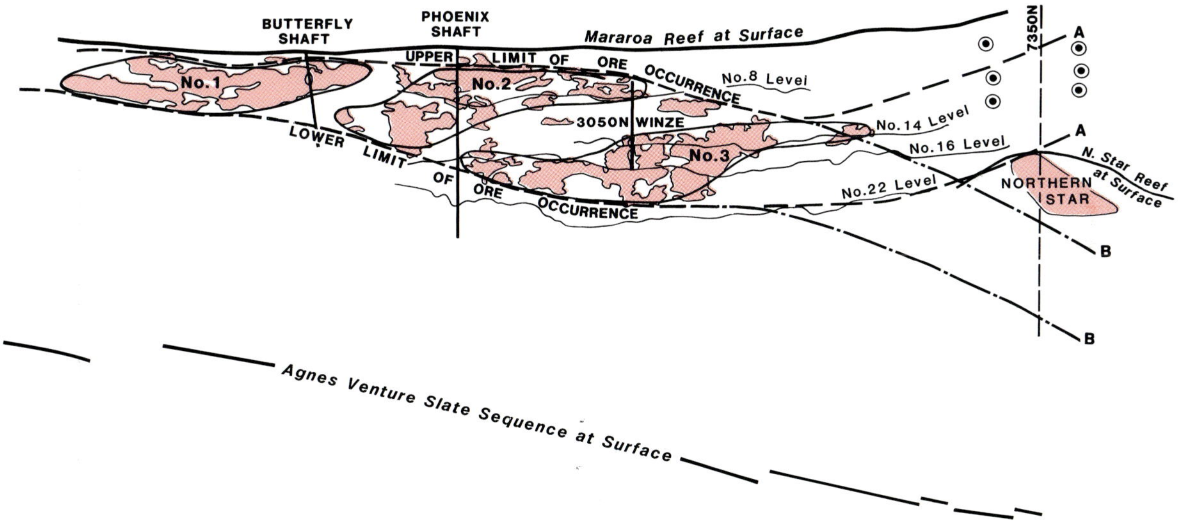

B. POSSIBLE ORE TRENDS AA AND BB

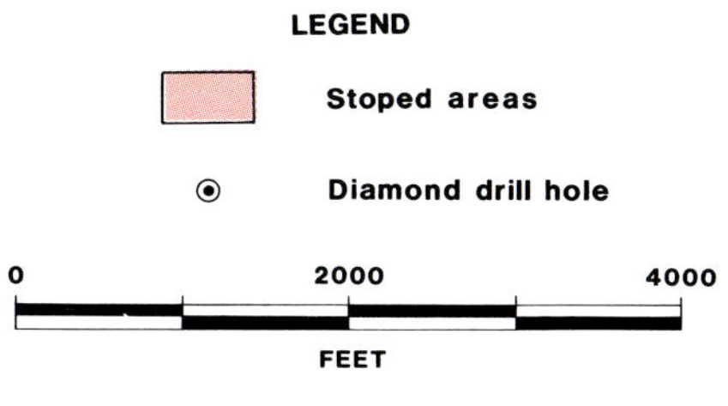

Plate 5 Plan projections of the Mararoa reef.
A. Development of No's 14, 16 and 22 levels, as at June 1946.
B. The limits of ore occurrence swinging upwards, dashed lines AA.
The limits of ore occurrence swinging downwards, dash-dot lines BB.

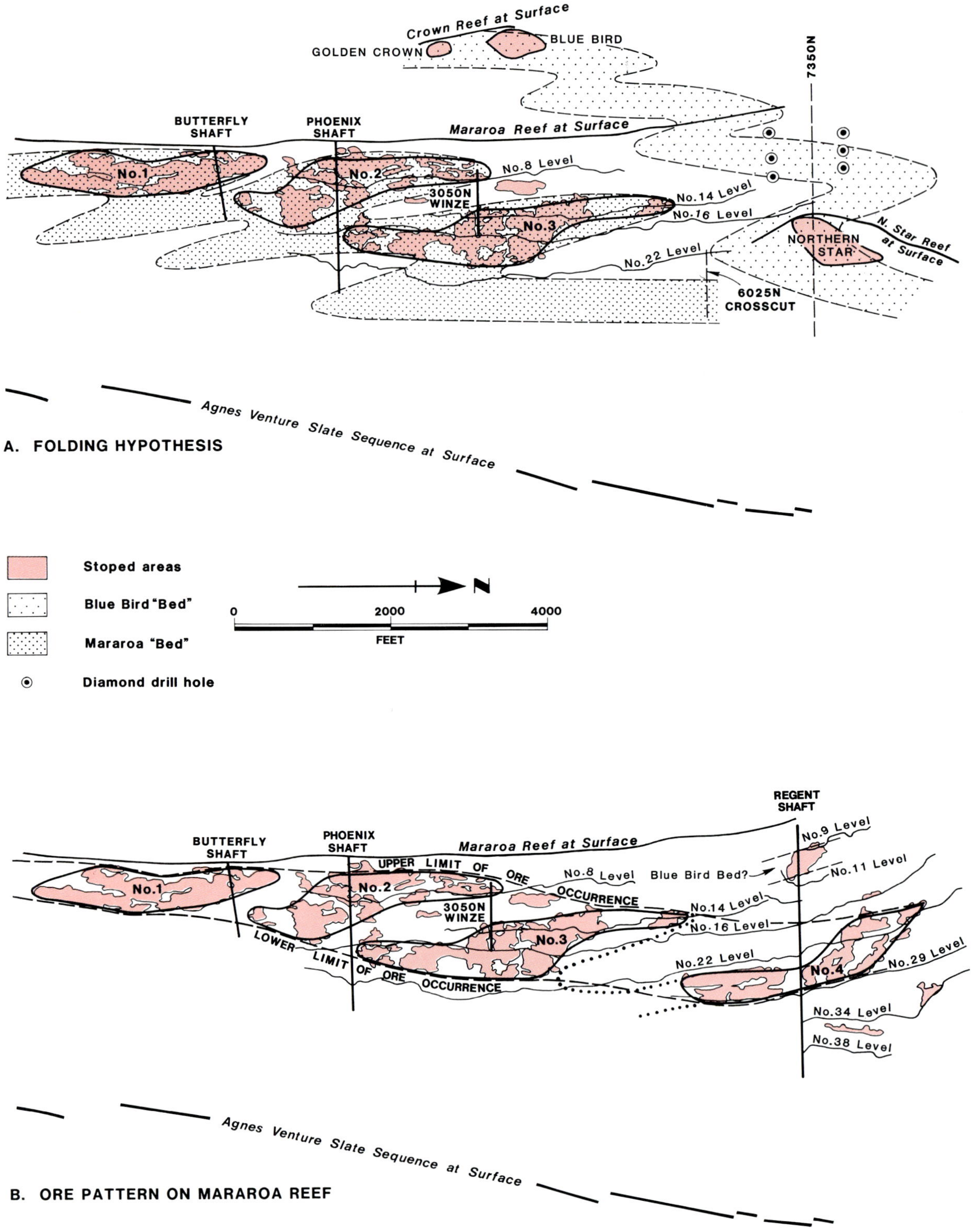

Plate 6

Plate 6 Plan projection of the Mararoa reef showing the folding hypothesis.

A. Hypothetical fold pattern — at the surface for the Blue Bird bed and on the Mararoa reef for the Mararoa bed.

B. The pattern of orebodies on the Mararoa reef. The over-all length of ore is 3.5 Kms.

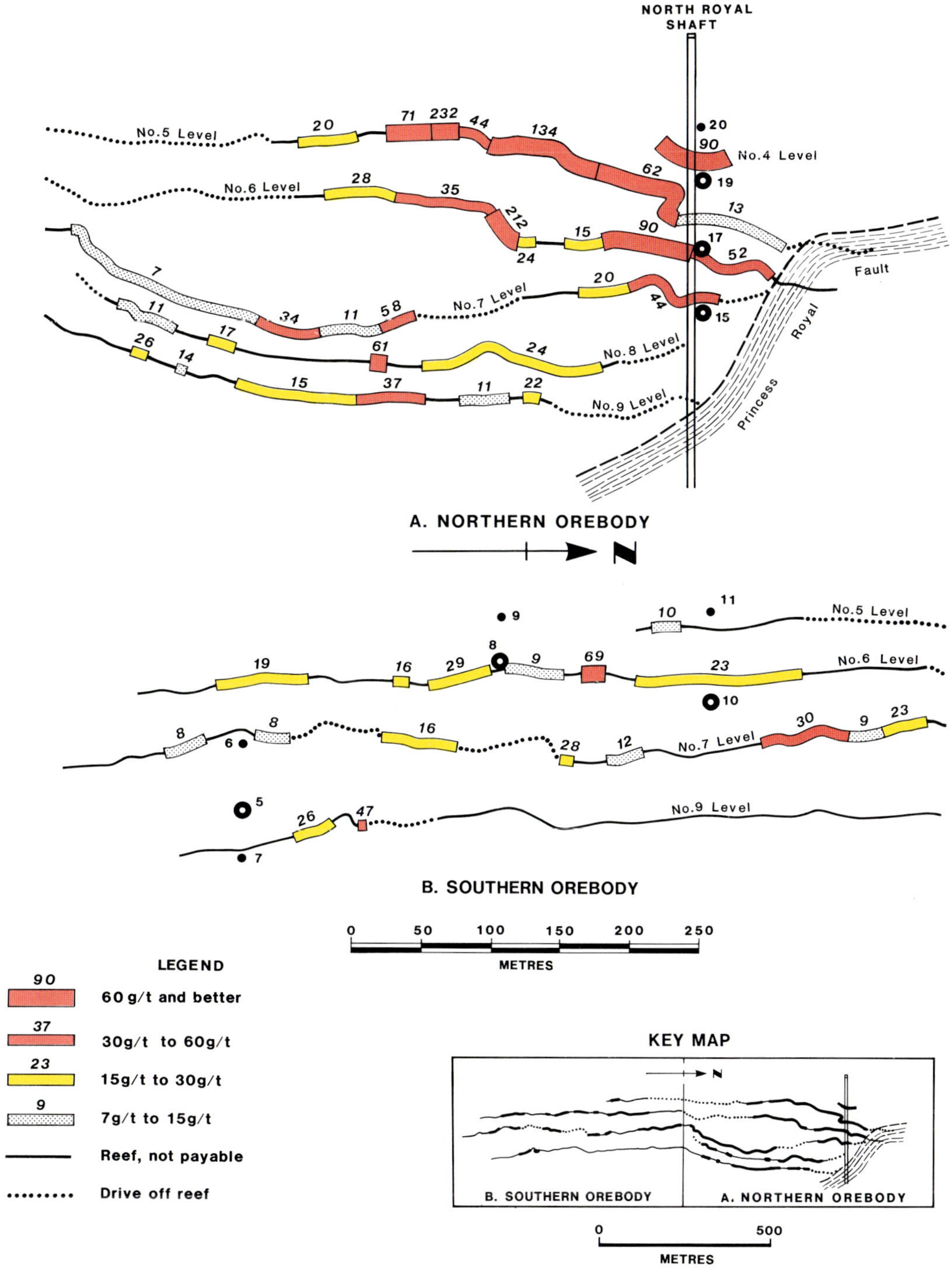

Plate 7 Plan projection showing assay runs and their average grades in the original underground openings at Princess Royal. The intersections in diamond drill holes PRS5 to PRS20 are shown in relation to the ore indicated by the various drives.

Plate 7

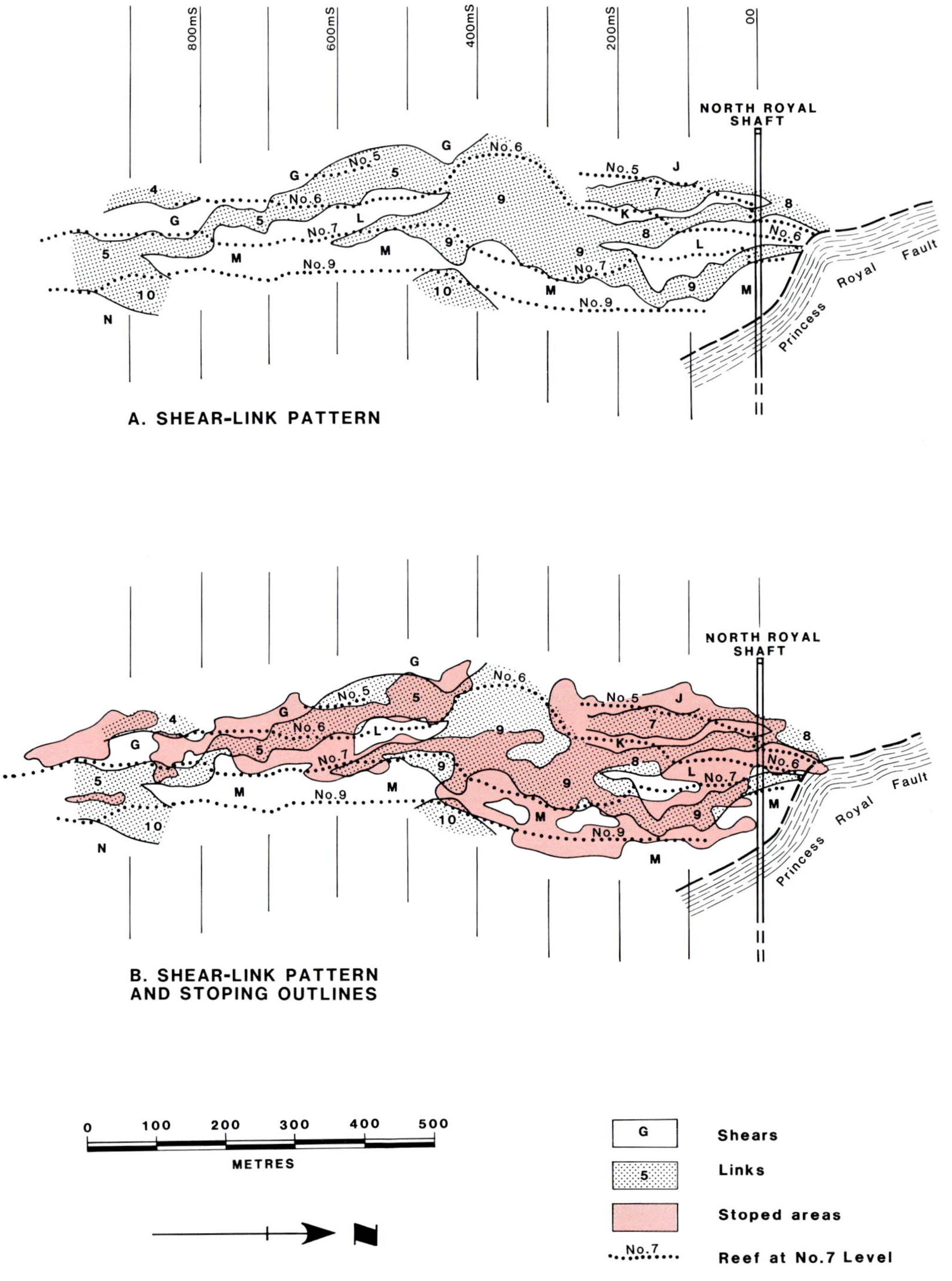

Plate 8

Plate 8 Plan projection of the original underground workings at Princess Royal.
A. Shear-link pattern.
B. Mined areas superimposed on the shear-link pattern.
Dotted lines show the course of the reef at No. 5, No. 6, No. 7 and No. 9 levels.

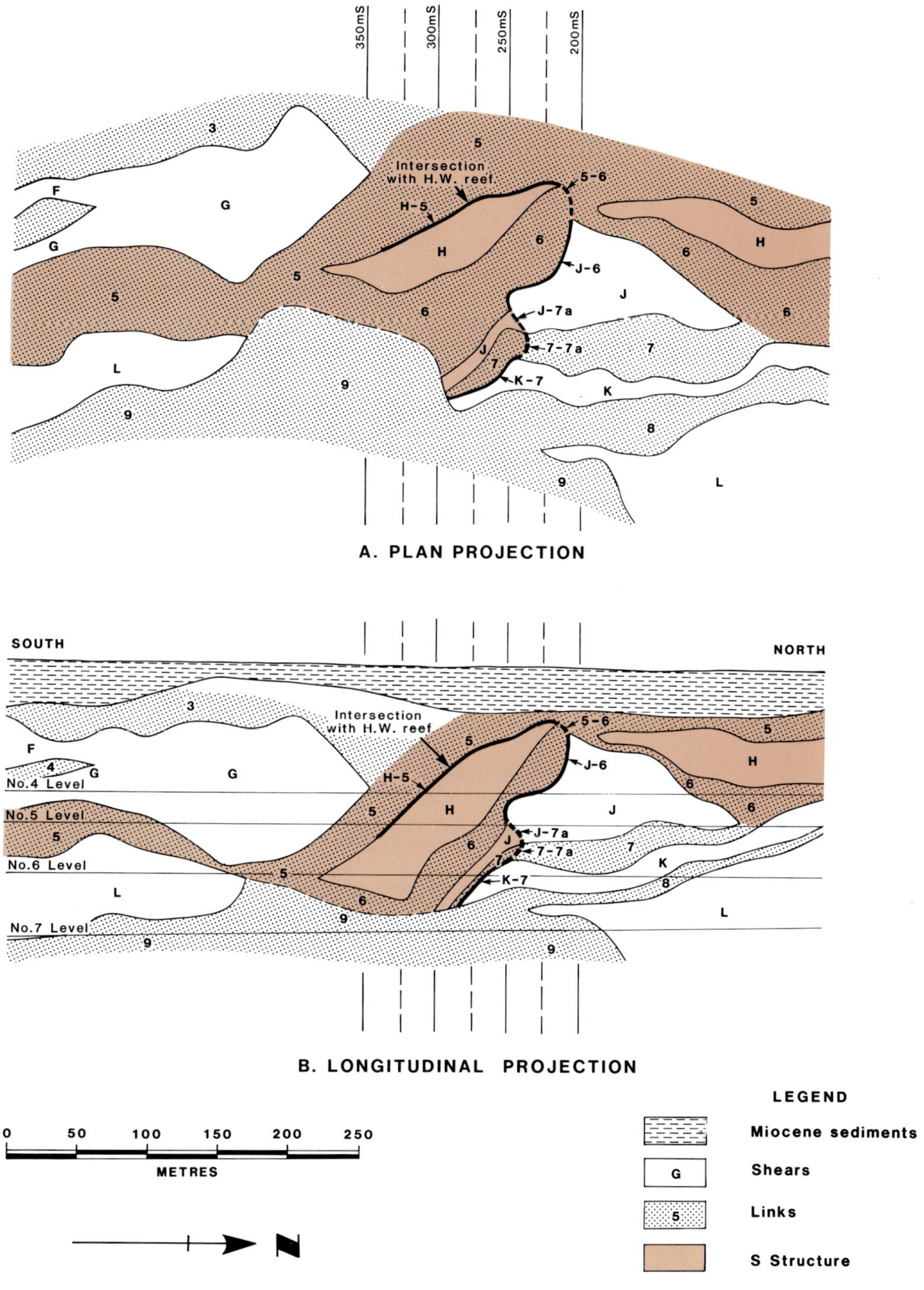

Plate 9 A. Plan projection and B. Longitudinal projection showing the S structure and the shear-link pattern of the foot-wall reef at Princess Royal. Clockwise, its intersection with the hanging-wall reef is: shear H — link 5, link 5 — link 6, shear J — link 6, shear J — link 7a, link 7 — link 7a, shear K — link 7.
The vein loop and the central core of the S structure "bottom" on link 9 (see Figure 30).

Plate 9

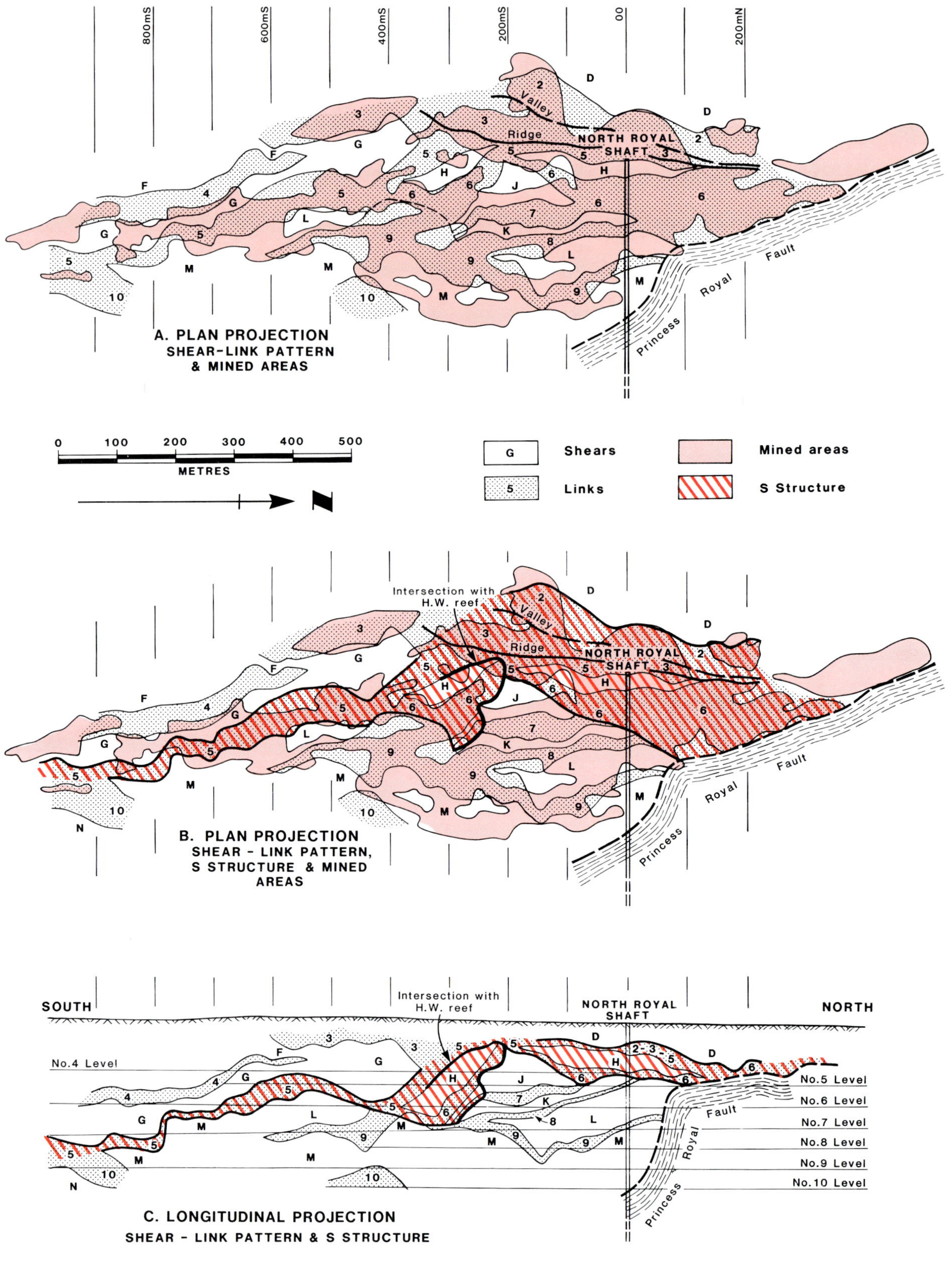

Plate 10

Plate 10 A. Plan projection showing mining (underground plus open-cuts) on the foot-wall reef at Princess Royal superimposed on the shear-link pattern of Figure 36.

B. Plate 10A repeated with the addition of the S structure which is shown in part in Plate 9A.

C. The S structure and the shear-link pattern in longitudinal projection. The overlap between the intersections shear M — link 9 and link 9 — link 6 is apparent, not real (see section 350mS, Figure 30).

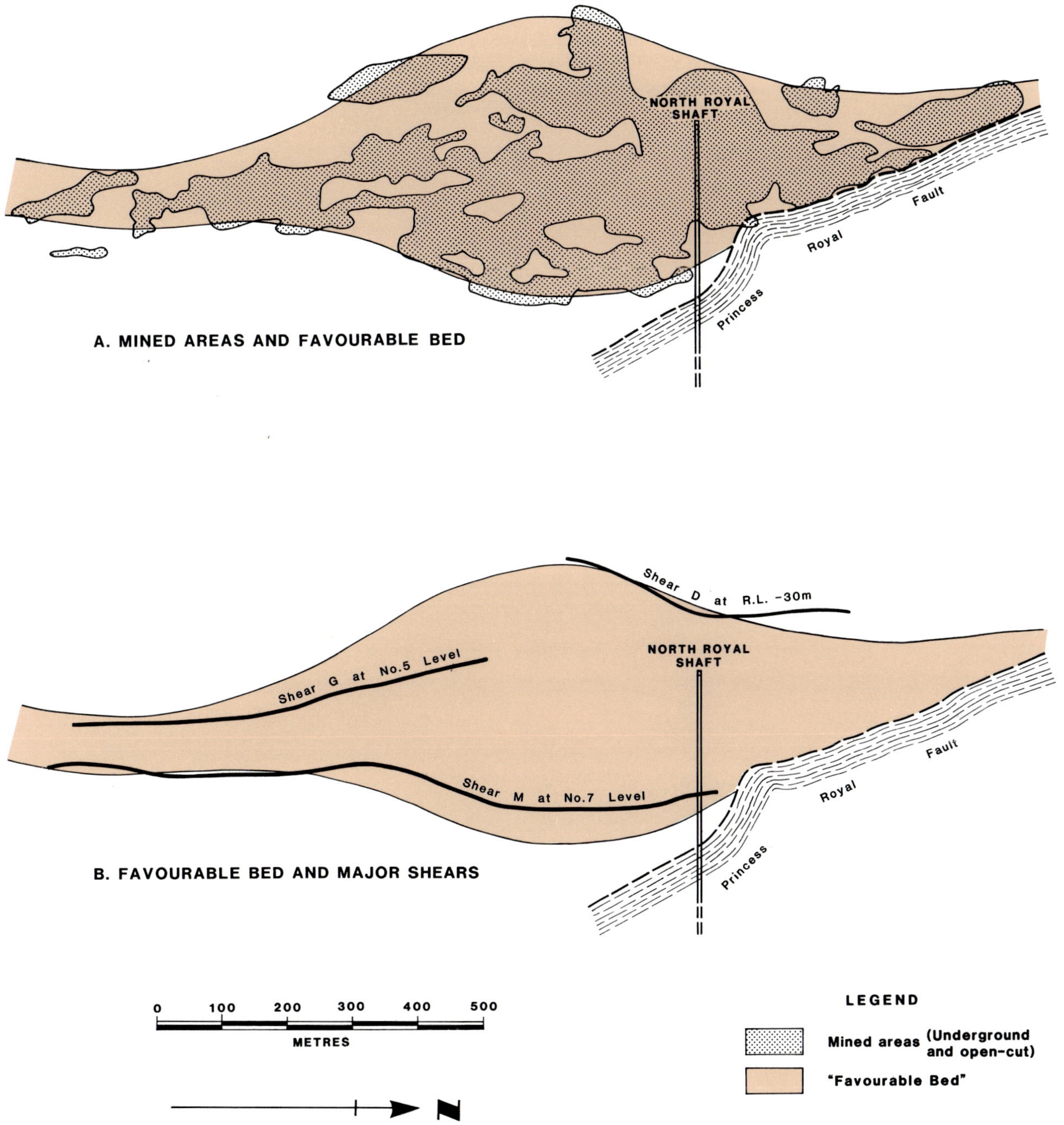

Plate 11 A. Plan projection showing the "favourable bed" needed to enclose the outline of the total area of mining on the foot-wall reef at Princess Royal.
B. Plan projection showing key shears in relation to this outline.

Plate 11

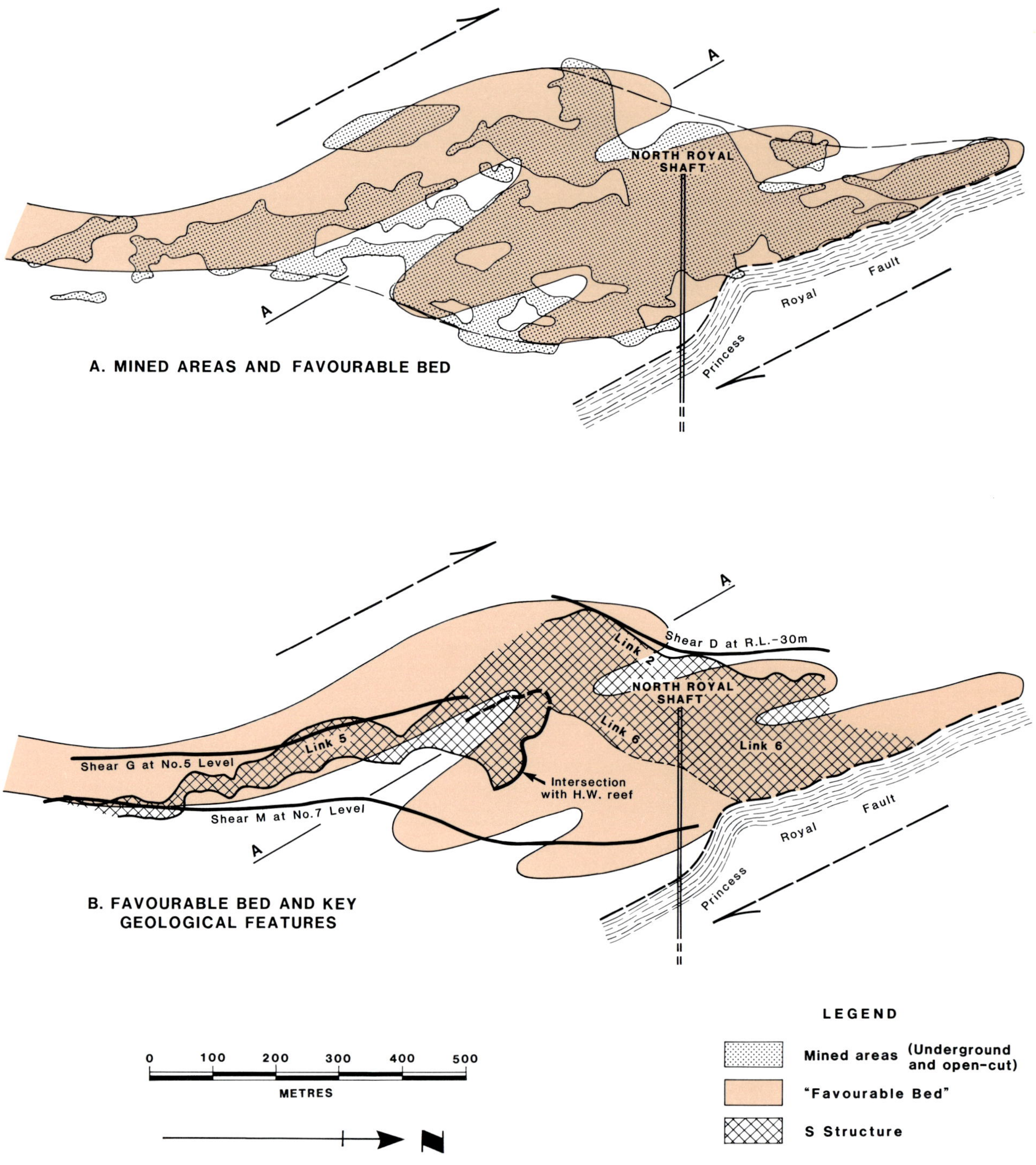

Plate 12

Plate 12 A. Plan projection showing the "favourable bed" of Plate 11A converted to a notional fold structure.

B. Plan projection showing key shears and the S structure superimposed on the fold pattern of Plate 12A.

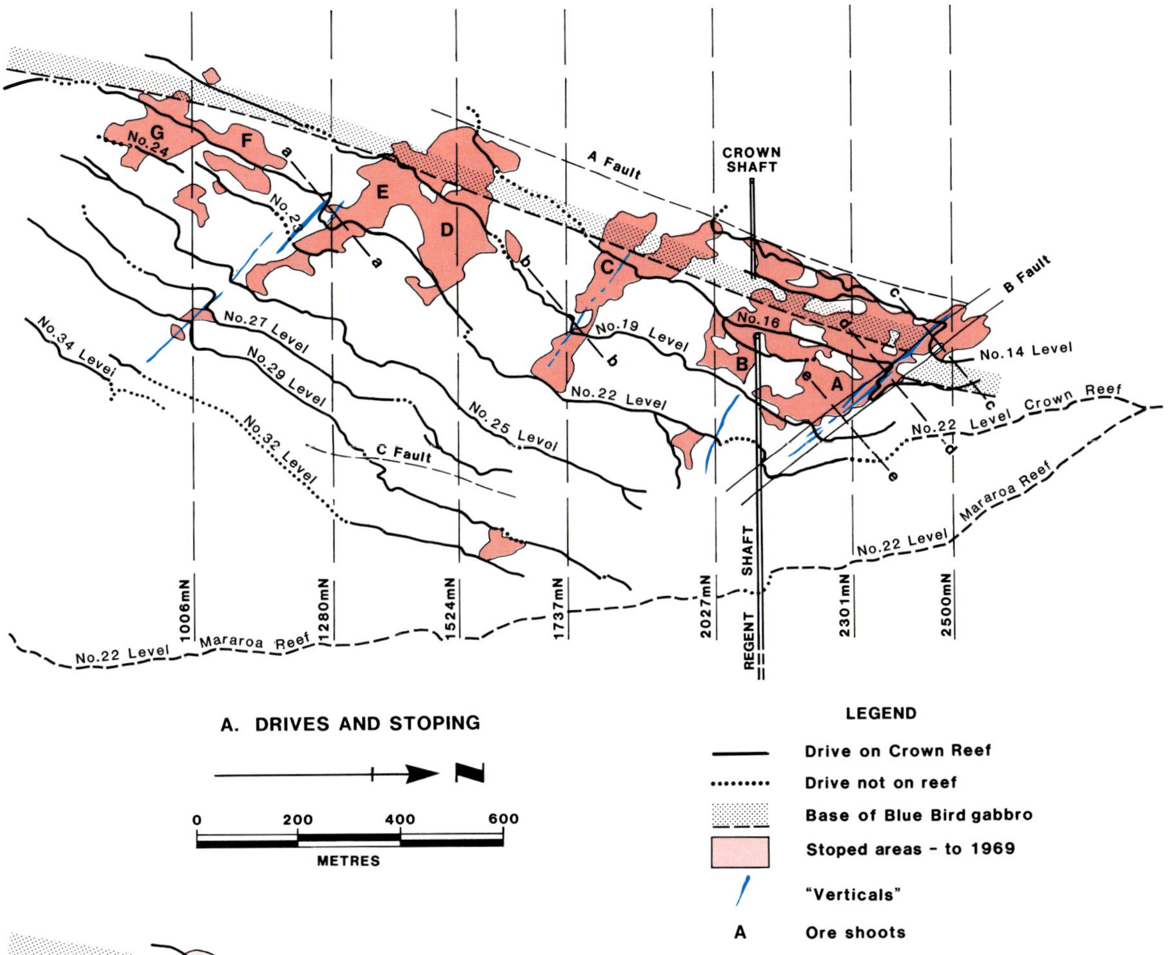

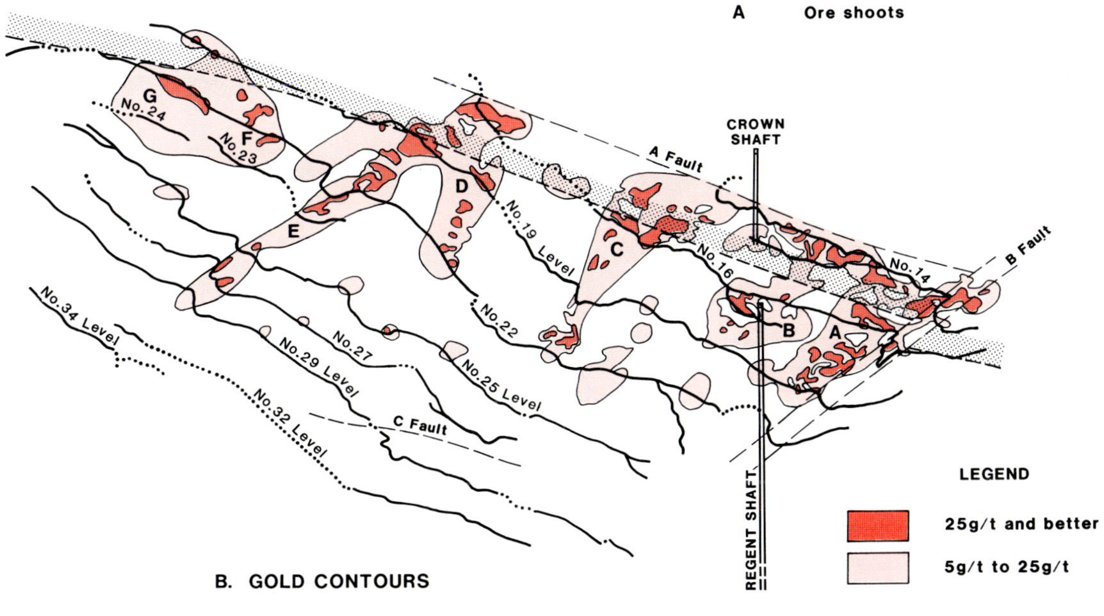

Plate 13 Plan projections showing the workings on the Crown reef.
A. Drives on the reef, stoping and its relationship to key geological features.
B. Gold contouring by R. Hewitt.

Plate 13

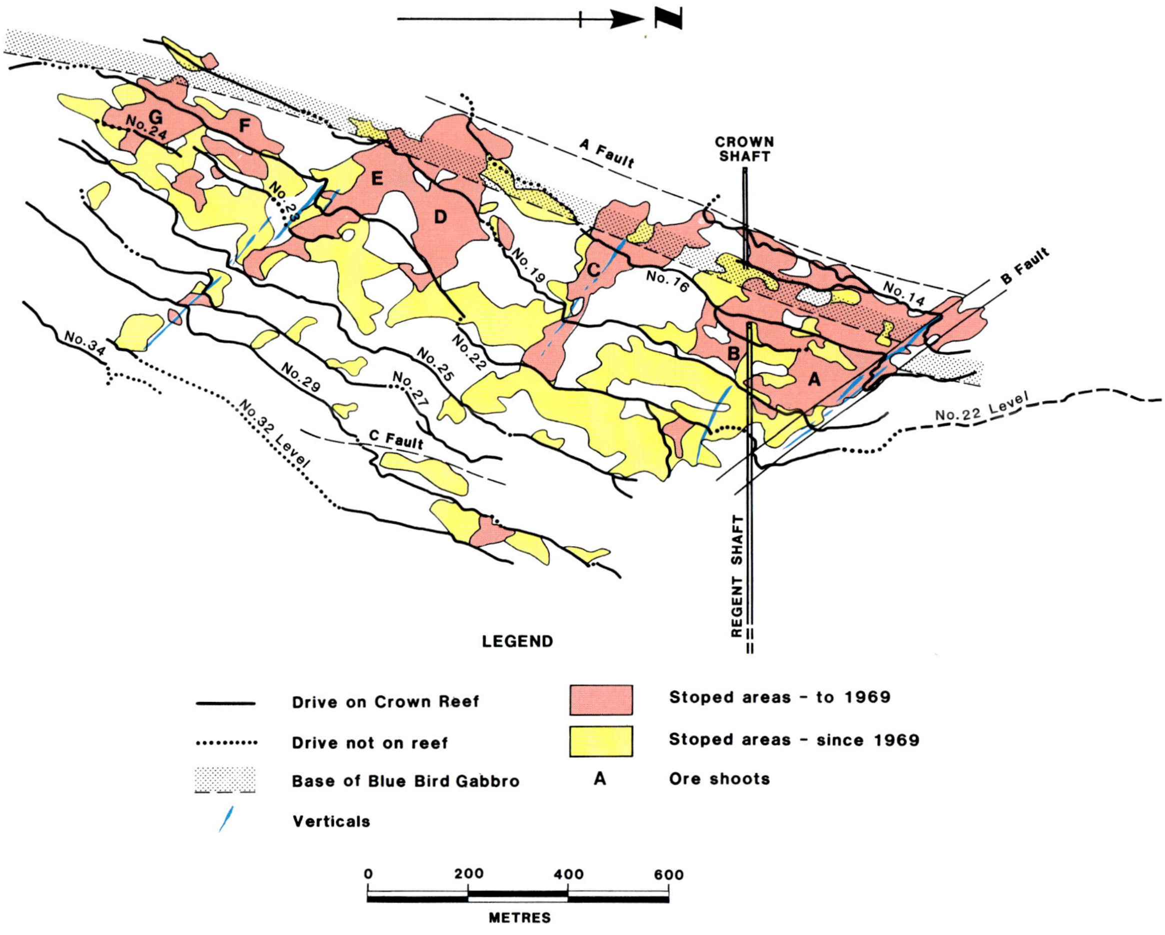

Plate 14

Plate 14 Plan projection of the Crown reef showing areas stoped to 1969 and the subsequent stoping of lower grade areas.

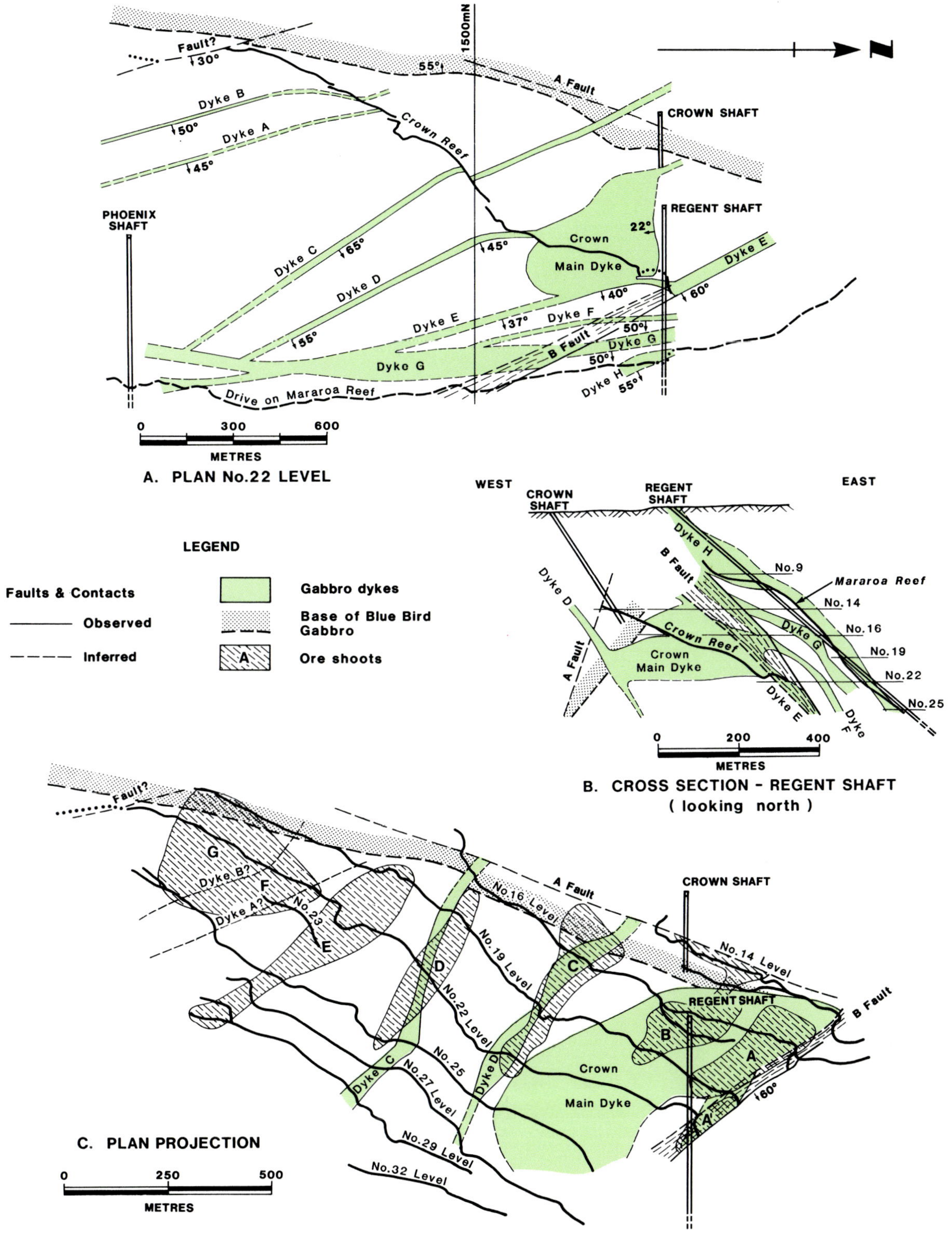

Plate 15 The Crown reef showing the interpretation by E. Cameron of the east-dipping gabbro dykes and, in Plate 15C, their relationship to ore occurrence.

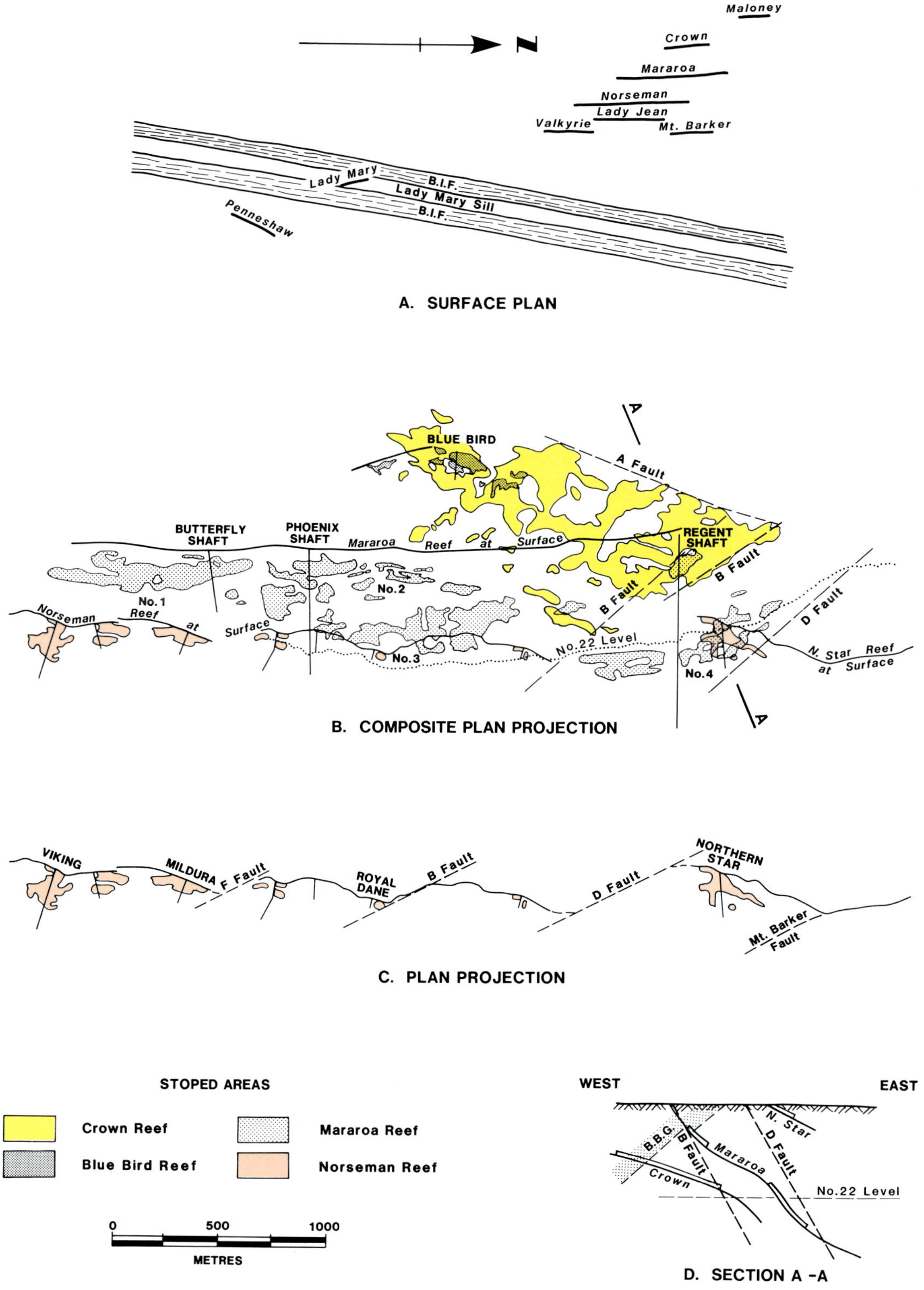

Plate 16

Plate 16 A. Surface plan showing the north-westerly trend of the reef outcrops at Norseman, H. King — Report K/555.

B. Composite plan showing stoped areas on the Blue Bird, Crown, Mararoa and Norseman reefs.

C. Plan projection showing the fault pattern on the Norseman reef and stoped areas.

D. Cross section looking north. The open "boxes" represent the extent of stoping. B.B.G., Blue Bird gabbro.

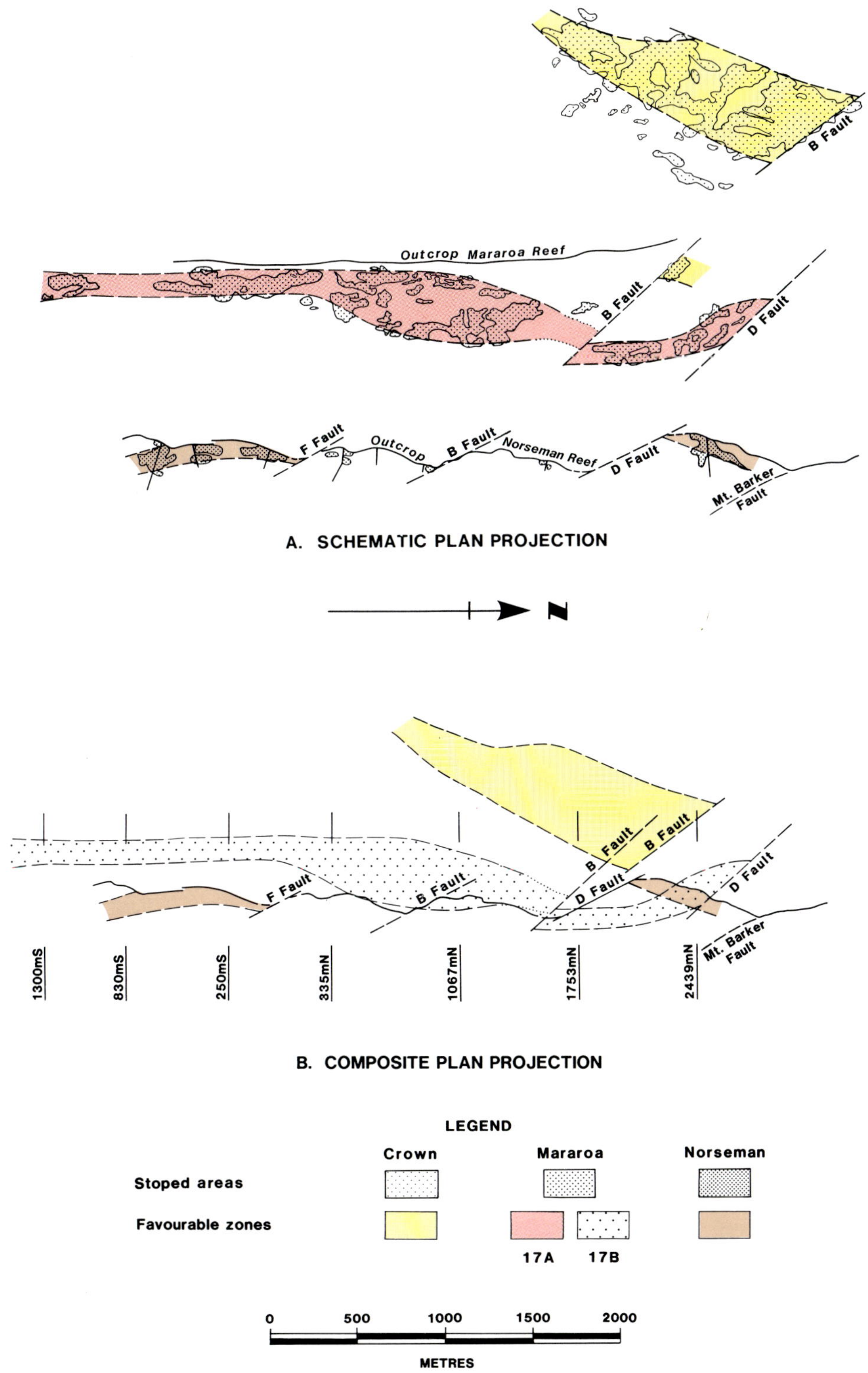

Plate 17 A. Schematic plan projection of the mined areas on the Crown, Mararoa and Norseman reefs aligned along the general trend of B fault.
B. Composite plan projection showing the favourable zones of Plate 17A in their true relative positions.

Plate 17

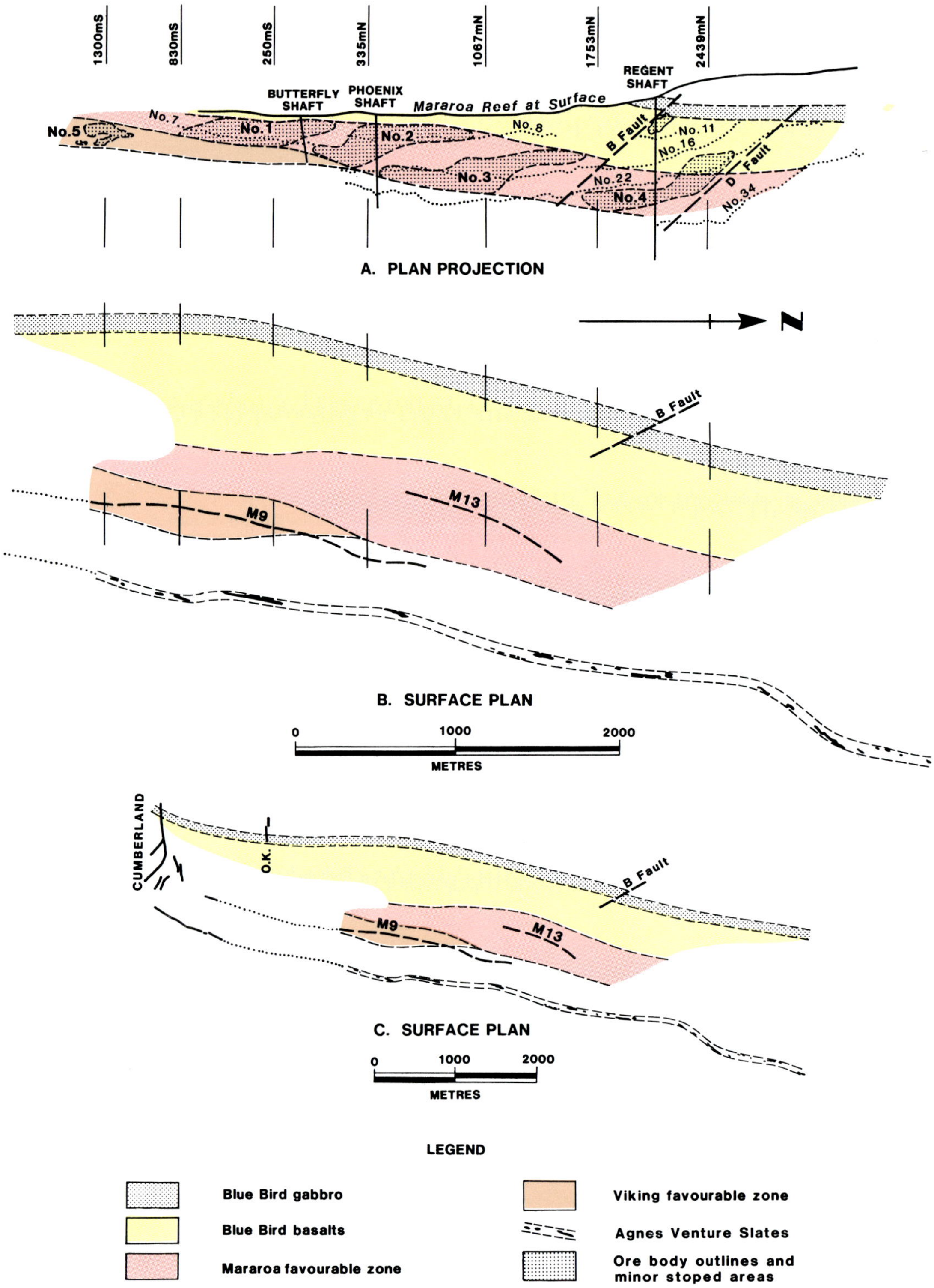

Plate 18

Plate 18 A. Plan projection of the Mararoa reef showing the orebodies and their relationship to the presumed favourable zone and to general geology.

B. Surface geological plan derived partly by projection upwards of the data presented in Plate 18A.

C. Plate 18B at a reduced scale with some extension to the north and a significant extension to the south.

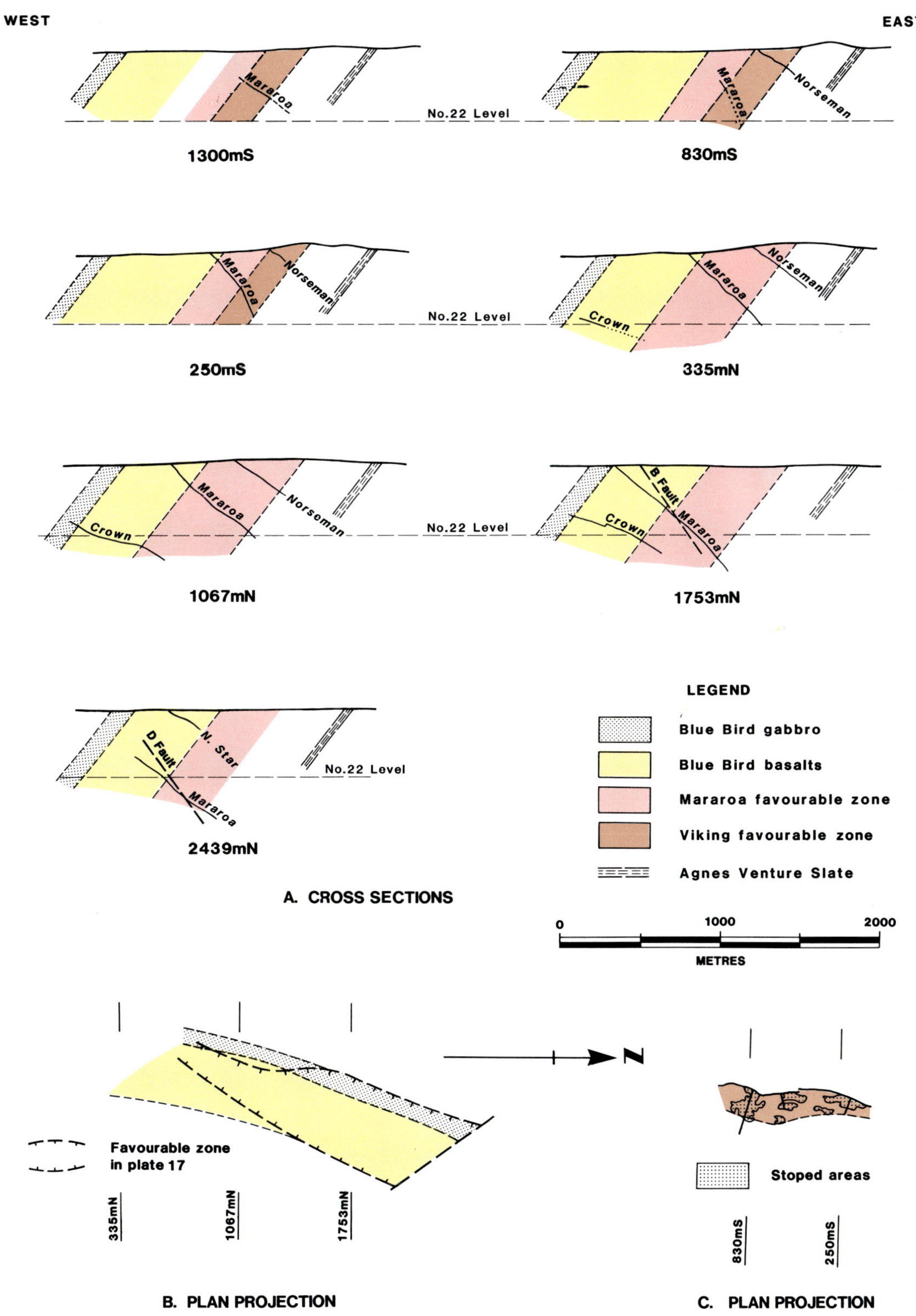

Plate 19 A. Cross sections relating to Plate 18 looking north.
B. Plan projection showing the Blue Bird basalt in relation to the Blue Bird favourable zone.
C. Plan projection showing the derivation of the Viking favourable zone.

Plate 19

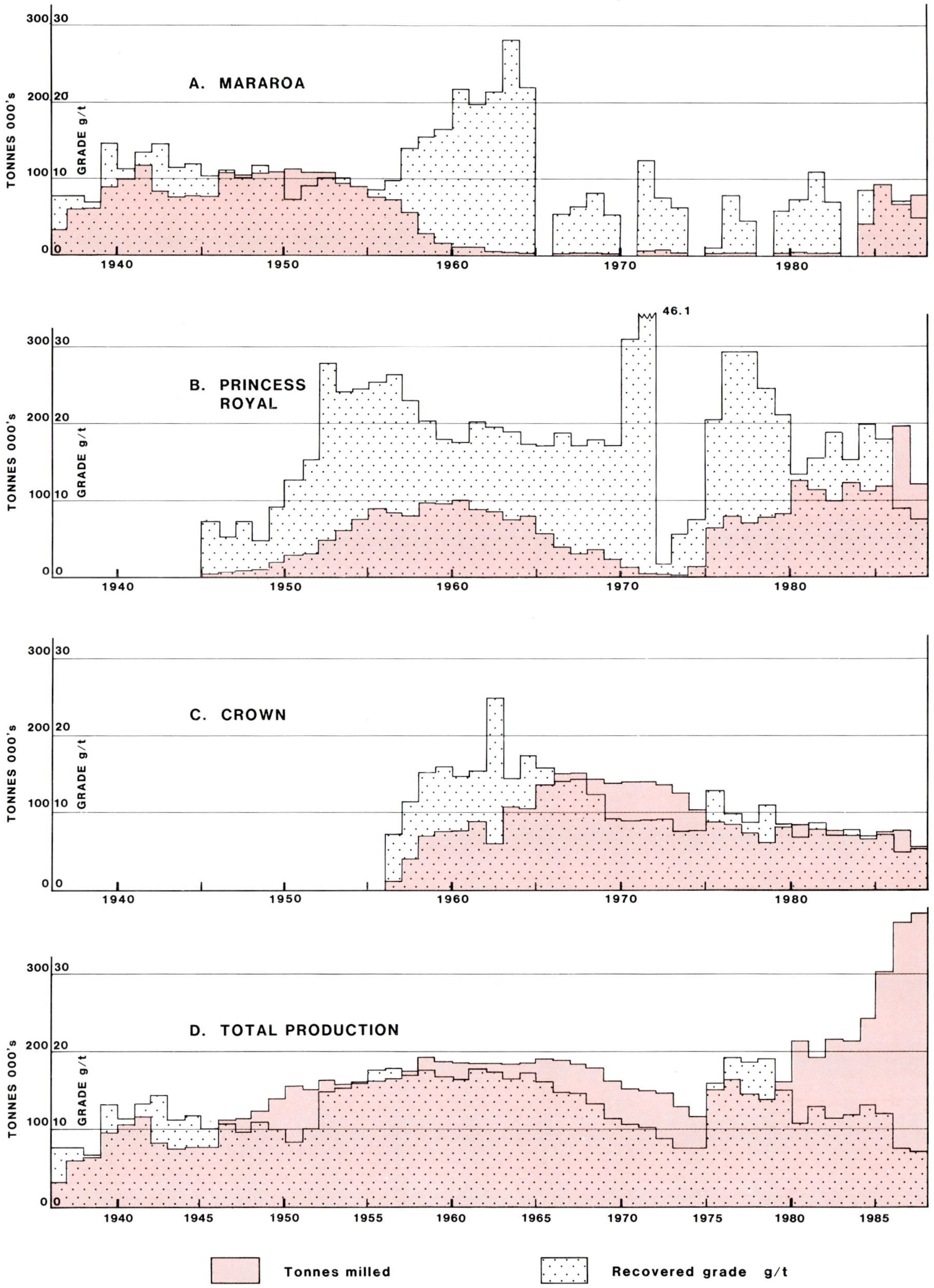

Plate 20

Plate 20 Production data for the years 1937-1988.